Ric Pimentel
Terry Wall

Cambridge
chec

NEW EDITION

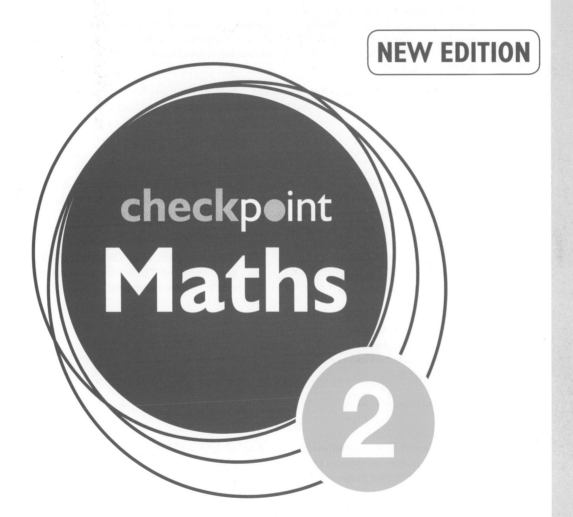

checkp●int
Maths

2

HODDER
EDUCATION
AN HACHETTE UK COMPANY

Acknowledgements

The authors and publishers would like to thank Adrian Metcalf for his help during the production of this book. The publishers would also like to thank the following for permission to reproduce copyright material.

Photo credits

p.1 © Karandaev – Fotolia; **p.2** © Mary Evans Picture Library; **p.32** © Angelika Bentin – Fotolia; **p.60** *tl* © Inmagine/Alamy, *tr* © FengYu/Fotolia.com, *bl* ©Graeme Dawes – Fotolia, *br* © Cheryl Casey – Fotolia; **p.73** © TebNad – Fotolia; **p.84** © The Art Archive/British Museum; **p.128** © MEDIUS – Fotolia; **p.189** © The Art Archive/British Museum; **p.209** © Absolut – Fotolia; **p.218** © FirstBlood – Fotolia

Every effort has been made to trace all copyright holders, but if any have been inadvertently overlooked the publishers will be pleased to make the necessary arrangements at the first opportunity.

Hachette UK's policy is to use papers that are natural, renewable and recyclable products and made from wood grown in well-managed forests and other controlled sources. The logging and manufacturing processes are expected to conform to the environmental regulations of the country of origin.

Orders: please contact Bookpoint Ltd, 130 Milton Park, Abingdon, Oxon OX14 4SB. Telephone: (44) 01235 827720. Fax: (44) 01235 400454. Lines are open 9.00–5.00, Monday to Saturday, with a 24-hour message answering service. Visit our website at www.hoddereducation.com

© Ric Pimentel and Terry Wall 2011
First published in 2011 by
Hodder Education, an Hachette UK Company,
Carmelite House, 50 Victoria Embankment,
London EC4Y 0DZ

Impression number   14
Year   2019

Cover photo © Massimo Listri/Corbis
Illustrations by Pantek Media and Barking Dog Art
Typeset in 11pt Palatino light by Pantek Media, Maidstone, Kent
Printed in India

A catalogue record for this title is available from the British Library

ISBN 978 1444 14397 3

Contents

The chapters in this book have been arranged to match the Cambridge Lower Secondary Mathematics curriculum framework for Stage 8 as follows:
- Number
- Algebra
- Geometry
- Measure
- Handling data
- Calculation and mental strategies
- Problem solving

● CONTENTS

Introduction

This series of books follows the Cambridge Lower Secondary Mathematics curriculum framework drawn up by Cambridge Assessment International Education. It has been written by two experienced teachers who have lived or worked in schools in many countries, and worked with teachers from other countries, including England, Spain, Germany, France, Turkey, South Africa, Malaysia and the USA.

Students and teachers in these countries come from a variety of cultures and speak many different languages as well as English. Sometimes cultural and language differences make understanding difficult. However, mathematics is largely free from these problems. Even a maths book written in Japanese will include algebra equations with x and y.

We should also all be very aware that much of the mathematics you will learn in these books was first discovered, and then built upon, by mathematicians from all over the world, including China, India, Arabia, Greece and Western countries.

Most early mathematics was simply game play and problem solving. Later this maths was applied to building, engineering and sciences of all kinds. Mathematicians study maths because they enjoy it.

We hope that you will enjoy the work you do, and the maths you learn in this series of books. Sometimes the ideas will not be easy to understand at first. That should be part of the fun. Ask for help if you need it, but try hard first. Write down what you are thinking so that others can understand what you have done and help to correct your mistakes. Most students think that maths is about answers, and so it is, but it is also a way to exercise our brains, whether we find the solution or not. Some questions throughout this book are starred (✪). This means that these questions go slightly beyond the content of the curriculum at this level and will be an enjoyable challenge for those of you who try them.

Ric Pimentel and Terry Wall

SECTION 1

◆ Read and write positive integer powers of 10; multiply and divide integers and decimals by 0.1, 0.01.

◆ Order decimals, including measurements, making use of the =, ≠, < and > signs.

◆ Round whole numbers to a positive integer power of 10 or decimals to the nearest whole number or one or two decimal places.

The word 'mathematics' comes from the Greek 'mathematika'. It is the study of patterns, including number patterns, and of shape and its structure, measurement and transformations.

Mathematics evolved through the use of logical reasoning. It moved from counting to calculating and measuring, and then to the study of shapes and the movement of objects.

The Greek mathematician Euclid is shown on the left. He lived in 300BC and is most famous for his work on geometry.

Place value and the decimal number system

Our number system is said to be 'base 10'. The position of each digit in a number determines its value. For example, 6287.48 can be placed in a table like this:

Thousands	Hundreds	Tens	Units	Tenths	Hundredths
6	2	8	7	4	8

the decimal point

Looking at the table, we can see that:

the 6 is worth   6000

the 2 is worth   200

the 8 is worth   80

the 7 is worth   7

the 4 is worth   0.4 or $\frac{4}{10}$

the 8 is worth   0.08 or $\frac{8}{100}$

We read the number 6287.48 as 'six thousand two hundred and eighty-seven point four eight'.

We do NOT say '... point forty-eight'.

Worked example

Read this number out loud:

4 628 370.52

You should say 'four million six hundred and twenty-eight thousand three hundred and seventy point five two'.

EXERCISE 1.1

1   Read these numbers out loud to a partner.

    a) 684 000   **b)** 3 420 000   **c)** 726 845.66

    d) 63 972.83   **e)** 543 210.98

2   Write these numbers in words.

    a) two hundred and fifty thousand

    b) eight million ten thousand six hundred

    c) three hundred and twelve thousand and six point two

    d) four hundred and eighty-seven point nine two six

    e) three million three thousand and three point three three

Rounding

Rounding to powers of 10

For integer values (whole numbers), it is often not necessary to give the exact number.

  For example, if a college has 5746 students, this figure can be rounded (approximated) in several ways by showing its position on a number line.

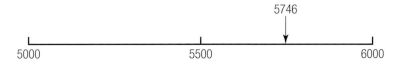

If 5746 is rounded to the nearest **thousand**, then it is written as 6000, because 5746 is closer to 6000 than it is to 5000.

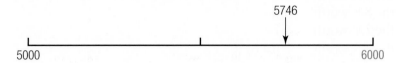

If 5746 is rounded to the nearest **hundred**, then it is written as 5700, because 5746 is closer to 5700 than it is to 5800.

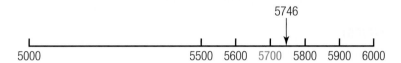

If 5746 is rounded to the nearest **ten**, then it is written as 5750, because 5746 is closer to 5750 than it is to 5740.

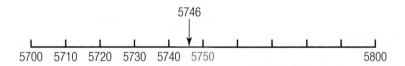

If a number is half way, then it is rounded up. For example, 5745 rounded to the nearest ten would be 5750 even though it is half way between 5740 and 5750.

Worked examples

77 648 people attended a recent football match in Milan.

a) This was reported in the programme as 80 000 attendance.
b) The club estimated that there were 78 000 people in the crowd.
c) A closer estimate in a newspaper was 77 650.

All of these estimates are acceptable. However, they are to different degrees of accuracy. Write down the degree of accuracy for each one.

a) nearest ten thousand
b) nearest thousand
c) nearest ten

EXERCISE 1.2A

1 Round each of these numbers to the degree of accuracy shown in brackets.
    a) 4865   (nearest ten)
    b) 7843   (nearest hundred)
    c) 18 695   (nearest thousand)
    d) 14 295   (nearest hundred)
    e) 684   (nearest ten)

f) 7346   (nearest hundred)
g) 899 200   (nearest hundred thousand)
h) 487 653   (nearest hundred thousand)
i) 3 478 000   (nearest million)
j) 4 562 700   (nearest million)

2   A survey showed that 14 627 cars went through a village on one Saturday.
     a) Round this number **(i)** to the nearest ten, **(ii)** to the nearest hundred and
        (iii) to the nearest thousand.
     b) Which number might be used by a local newspaper campaigning for a
        safe crossing to be built in the village?

3   A village hall holds 567 people.
     a) Round this number to the nearest hundred.
     b) What would you say is its **safe capacity** to the nearest hundred?

4   The rock band Muse played in front of 106 348 people in China.
     Round this number to the nearest hundred thousand.

5   From London to Boston is 4827 km.
     Round this distance to the nearest 100 km.

6   A company made a profit of $687 250.
     Round this amount to the nearest $10 000.

7   The table shows the capacities of some of the largest sports stadiums in the
     world. With a partner, round the number for the capacity of each stadium
     to the nearest thousand.

Stadium	Sport	Capacity
Rungrado May Day Stadium – Pyongyang, North Korea	Association football	150 000
Salt Lake Stadium – Kolkata, India	Association football	119 750
Michigan Stadium – Ann Arbor, USA	American football	109 901
Estadio Azteca – Mexico City, Mexico	Association football	100 607
Melbourne Cricket Ground – Melbourne, Australia	Cricket, Association football	100 018
Azadi Stadium – Tehran, Iran	Association football	100 126
Camp Nou – Barcelona, Spain	Association football	98 787
FNB Stadium – Johannesburg, South Africa	Association football	94 700
Gelora Bung Karno Stadium – Jakarta, Indonesia	Association football	88 306
Bukit Jalil National Stadium – Kuala Lumpur, Malaysia	Association football	87 411
Estádio do Maracanã – Rio de Janeiro, Brazil	Association football	82 238

Decimal places

If 6287.48 is rounded to the nearest whole number, then it is written as 6287, and to one decimal place it rounds up to 6287.5.

This method can be extended in order to round a number to two decimal places.

For example, if the number 6287.483 is rounded to two decimal places, the third digit after the decimal point is 3 so it rounds down to 6287.48. But in the number 6287.487, the third digit after the decimal point is 7 so it rounds up to 6287.49.

Numbers can be rounded to any number of decimal places. This can be shown clearly by using a number line.

Worked example

The length of a model car is 5.864 cm.
Write 5.864 to two decimal places.
Draw a number line to help you.

A number written to two decimal places has two digits after the decimal point.

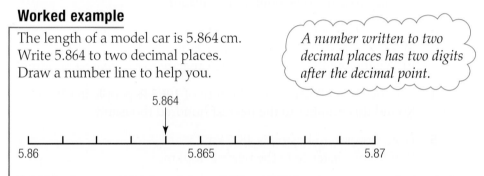

5.864 is closer to 5.86 than it is to 5.87, so 5.864 written to two decimal places is 5.86.

> To round to the nearest whole number (integer) or to a certain number of decimal places, look at the next digit after the one in question. If that digit is 5 or more, round up. If it is 4 or less, round down.

EXERCISE 1.2B

Round each of the following numbers **(i)** to the nearest whole number, **(ii)** to one decimal place and **(iii)** to two decimal places.

a) 8.757	**b)** 7.492	**c)** 18.685	**d)** 0.1238	**e)** 4.856
f) 9.470	**g)** 12.3852	**h)** 9.2563	**i)** 14.7777	**j)** 0.6666

Rounding up or rounding down

The usual rule for rounding is that if the digit after the one in question is 5 or more, you round up. If it is 4 or less, you round down. For example,

1.7 to the nearest whole number is 2.
5.72 to one decimal place is 5.7.
5.75 to one decimal place is 5.8.
0.07 to one decimal place is 0.1.

But in Student's Book 1 you saw that you need to use common sense too.

Worked example

A bridge is 4.7 m high. A sign needs to be put on the bridge to warn drivers.

Would you say that 'Maximum height 5 m' or 'Maximum height 4 m' is the best sign?

Rounded to the nearest whole number, the maximum height would be given as 5 m.

But somebody driving a bus 4.8 m tall would not be helped by rounding up. The bus would crash.

So 'Maximum height 4 m' is a more useful sign.

EXERCISE 1.2C

1 A bridge can safely carry a weight of 11.75 tonnes.
   Round this weight sensibly to a whole number of tonnes.
   Write a warning sign.

2 A pilot needs to know the height of a mountain the aircraft is to fly over.
   The mountain is 6.35 km high. Round this height appropriately:
   a) to a whole number of kilometres
   b) to one decimal place.

3 An aqualung will work safely to a depth of 67.3 metres.
   What rounded figure would you use as the safe working depth?

4 A stadium has 76 890 seats.
   What would you say was its maximum capacity:
   a) to a whole thousand   **b)** to a whole hundred?

5 A bridge is to be built over a river 2315 m wide.
   Write down a sensible estimate of its length, to a whole 100 m, for working out how much steel will be needed.

When dividing, you may need to decide whether it is more sensible to round up or to round down.

Worked example

A car transporter can carry eight cars.
How many transporters are needed for 60 cars?
$$60 \div 8 = 7.5$$

Therefore 8 transporters will be needed.

In fact, 8 transporters will be needed for any number of cars from 57 up to and including 64.

EXERCISE 1.2D

1 A plane can carry 8.5 tonnes of cargo. Each container weighs 1.75 tonnes.
How many containers can the plane carry safely?

2 A baker makes loaves weighing 600 g.
How many loaves can she make from 12.9 kg of dough?

3 Wooden houses are being built on a concrete base.
Each base needs 400 kg of concrete.
A cement truck carries 9 tonnes of concrete.
How many bases can be laid from one truck-load of concrete?

4 Houses are built with wooden panels. Each house needs 15 panels.
How many houses can be built from 1000 panels?

5 A ship can carry 12 000 tonnes of cargo. A container weighs 14 tonnes.
How many containers can the ship carry safely?

Multiplying and dividing integers by 0.1 and 0.01

You know that $0.1 = \frac{1}{10}$.

So multiplying by 0.1 is the same as multiplying by $\frac{1}{10}$. For example,

$$740 \times 0.1 = 740 \times \frac{1}{10} = 74$$

But $740 \div 10 = 74$.
So multiplying by 0.1 is the same as multiplying by $\frac{1}{10}$ and as dividing by 10.
Similarly, $0.01 = \frac{1}{100}$.
So multiplying by 0.01 is the same as multiplying by $\frac{1}{100}$ and as dividing by 100.

Worked examples

a) Work out
450×0.1

$450 \times 0.1 = 450 \div 10 = 45$

b) Work out
352×0.1

$352 \times 0.1 = 352 \div 10 = 35.2$

c) Work out
8370×0.01

$8370 \times 0.01 = 8370 \div 100 = 83.7$

d) Work out
524×0.01

$524 \times 0.01 = 524 \div 100 = 5.24$

EXERCISE 1.3A

Work out the following multiplications without using a calculator.

1	360×0.1	**2**	850×0.1	**3**	1460×0.1
4	5600×0.1	**5**	8760×0.1	**6**	2360×0.01
7	1850×0.01	**8**	5600×0.01	**9**	1460×0.01
10	875×0.01	**11**	62×0.01	**12**	153×0.01
13	7244×0.01	**14**	27×0.1	**15**	38×0.01

Since $0.1 = \frac{1}{10}$, dividing by 0.1 is the same as dividing by $\frac{1}{10}$.

But dividing by $\frac{1}{10}$ is the same as multiplying by 10.

So dividing by 0.1 is the same as dividing by $\frac{1}{10}$ and as multiplying by 10.

Similarly, $0.01 = \frac{1}{100}$, so dividing by 0.01 is the same as dividing by $\frac{1}{100}$.

But dividing by $\frac{1}{100}$ is the same as multiplying by 100.

So dividing by 0.01 is the same dividing by $\frac{1}{100}$ and as multiplying by 100.

Worked examples

a) Work out
$$7.3 \div 0.1$$

$$7.3 \div 0.1 = 7.3 \times 10 = 73$$

b) Work out
$$84.62 \div 0.01$$

$$84.62 \div 0.01 = 84.62 \times 100 = 8462$$

c) Work out
$$5.02 \div 0.1$$

$$5.02 \div 0.1 = 5.02 \times 10 = 50.2$$

d) Work out
$$0.39 \div 0.01$$
$$0.39 \div 0.01 = 0.39 \times 100 = 39$$

EXERCISE 1.3B

Work out the following divisions without using a calculator.

1 $5.9 \div 0.1$

2 $17.2 \div 0.1$

3 $0.6 \div 0.1$

4 $0.87 \div 0.1$

5 $14.03 \div 0.1$

6 $18.82 \div 0.01$

7 $5.43 \div 0.01$

8 $0.792 \div 0.01$

9 $5.3 \div 0.1$

10 $0.3 \div 0.1$

11 $0.03 \div 0.1$

12 $0.07 \div 0.01$

13 $6 \div 0.1$

14 $20 \div 0.01$

15 $0.6666 \div 0.01$

16 A 10 cent coin is worth $0.10.
   How many 10 cent coins are there in $8?

17 A piece of wood 2 m 30 cm long is marked off into 0.1 m lengths.
   How many 0.1 m lengths are there?

18 A car travels 0.5 km on 0.01 litre of fuel.
   How many kilometres will it travel on 40 litres of fuel?

Inequalities

You are familiar with the sign =, which means 'is equal to'. Another sign is ≠, which means 'is not equal to'. Two other useful signs are > meaning 'is greater than' and < meaning 'is less than'.

These signs can be used to describe the relationship between numbers and quantities.

For example,

   $4 \times 5 < 3 \times 8$ means 4×5 is less than 3×8.   *Since 20 < 24*

EXERCISE 1.4A

Copy and complete the following statements, writing one of the signs =, > or < to make each statement true.

1 5×3 _____ 7×2

2 $6 + 5$ _____ 4×3

3 $8 + 8$ _____ 4×4

4 70 cm _____ 1 m

5 70 cm _____ 0.7 m

6 10 cm _____ 1000 mm

7 10 m _____ 100 cm

8 4 tonnes _____ 3500 kg

9 $5 \times 5 \times 5$ _____ 20×5

10 8×0.1 _____ $8 \div 10$

Ordering integers and decimals

Worked example

Write the following numbers in order of size, smallest first.
Use the symbol < (less than).
$$0.4, \quad 0.04, \quad 4, \quad 3.8, \quad 0.38, \quad 0.06, \quad 0.038$$

The order can be found by writing the numbers in a place value table.

Tens	Units	•	Tenths	Hundredths	Thousandths
	0	•	4		
	0	•	0	4	
	4	•			
	3	•	8		
	0	•	3	8	
	0	•	0	6	
	0	•	0	3	8

Working from left to right in the table, the correct order is:
$$0.038 < 0.04 < 0.06 < 0.38 < 0.4 < 3.8 < 4$$

EXERCISE 1.4B

Write each of the following sets of numbers in order of size, smallest first.
Use the symbol for 'less than' in your answers.

1 0.8,   0.6,   0.84,   0.09,   1,   0.49

2 0.36,   3.6,   3,   6.3,   0.6,   0.09

Make a place value table if necessary.

3 4,   4.4,   0.44,   0.4,   44,   0.04

4 6,   0.6,   6.6,   0.66,   0.06,   0.066

5 3.3,   0.3,   0.33,   3.33,   3.03,   0.333

2 Expressions, equations and formulae

◆ Know that letters play different roles in equations, formulae and functions; know the meanings of *formula* and *function*.

◆ Know that algebraic operations, including brackets, follow the same order as arithmetic operations.

◆ Construct linear expressions.

◆ Simplify or transform linear expressions with integer coefficients; collect like terms; multiply a single term over a bracket.

You already know that letters are often used when working with expressions, equations, formulae and functions.

You should already know that an **expression** is used to represent a value in algebraic form. For example,

The length of the line is given by the expression $x + 6$.

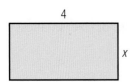

The perimeter of the rectangle is given by the expression $x + 4 + x + 4$.

This can be simplified to $2x + 8$.

In the examples above, x, $2x$ and 8 are called **terms** in the expressions.

In the expression $2a + 3b + 4c - 5$, each of $2a$, $3b$, $4c$ and -5 is a term in the expression.

An expression is different from an **equation**. An equation contains an equals sign (=), which shows that the expressions either side of it are equal to each other. For example, the equation

$$x + 1 = y - 2$$

tells us that the expressions $x + 1$ and $y - 2$ are equal to each other.

An equation represents two quantities which are equal to each other. To help to see what an equation is and how it can be used, it is useful to look at it as a pair of scales.

Worked example

The mass of each of the small objects is 1 kg. Write an equation in terms of x.

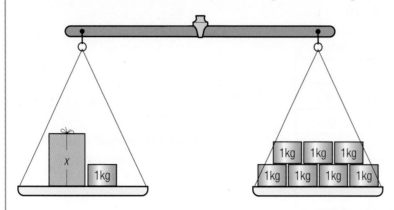

Because the scales are balanced, the objects on the left-hand side of the scales must weigh the same as those on the right-hand side.

The equation is

$$x + 1 = 7$$

With an equation, there is one or more values of the variable that make it correct. In the example above, $x = 6$.

A **formula** also has an equals sign (=). It describes the relationship between different variables. In the earlier example, the perimeter of the rectangle was written as $2x + 8$. This can be written as the formula $P = 2x + 8$, where P represents the perimeter. The formula will produce different values of P depending on the value of x.

In Student's Book 1 you saw some **function machines** like this:

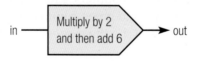

A **function** is similar to both an equation and a formula in that it describes the relationship between two variables. It describes how each value of the input variable is linked to an output. A function always gives an output value.
Using algebra, we can write the function above as:

$$f(x) = 2x + 6.$$

Worked example

Calculate the output of the function $f(x) = 2x + 6$ for each of the input values $x = 1, 2, 3, 4, 5, 6$.

Input	Output
1	8
2	10
3	12
4	14
5	16
6	18

To find the output when $x = 4$, for example, we can write $f(4) = 2 \times 4 + 6 = 14$.

Constructing expressions

It is important to be able to construct expressions from information that is given. For example, suppose that we have some full boxes of counters.

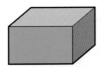 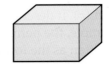 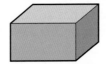 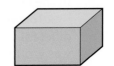

The boxes contain red, yellow, blue and green counters respectively (it does not matter yet how many counters there are in each box). We can use the letter r to stand for the number of counters in a full box of red counters, y for a full box of yellow counters, and b and g for full boxes of blue and green counters respectively.

If there are 3 full boxes of red counters we can write the expression $3r$ for the total number of red counters.

If there are 3 full boxes of red counters and 5 extra red counters, the total number of red counters can be written as $3r + 5$.

EXERCISE 2.1A

Write an expression for the total number of counters in each of these cases.

1 3 full boxes of red counters and 2 full boxes of blue counters

2 1 full box of red counters, 3 full boxes of green counters and 5 full boxes of yellow counters

3 4 full boxes of blue counters and 7 extra blue counters

4 1 box of yellow counters from which 5 counters have been removed

5 1 box of blue counters from which 25 counters have been removed and then the remaining number has been doubled

Expressions can also be written from information that is given on a diagram.
   In the diagram the lengths of the sides are shown with letters.
   The perimeter of the shape is therefore
$$m + n + m + n + m + n + m + n.$$

This can be simplified to $4m + 4n$.

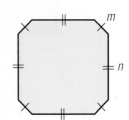

EXERCISE 2.1B

Simplify the following expressions.

1 $2a + 3a + 5a$

2 $4b - 2b + 7b$

3 $3c + 8 - 5c + 7 + 8c$

4 $4d - 5 + 8 - 2d$

5 $3e + 8e + 7 - e$

6 $6f - 7f - 3 + 4f - 8$

7 $4g + 6 - 8g - 9$

8 $3h - 7 - 9h + 11$

9 $6i - 3i - 14 + 9i - 4$

10 $3j - 4 + 8j - 11 - j$

EXERCISE 2.1C

For each of the shapes in questions 1–5:
a) write a simplified expression for the perimeter
b) derive a formula for the perimeter in the form $P = ...$

> The perimeter is the distance around a shape.

1

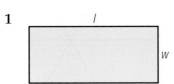

2

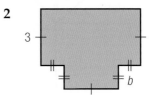

3

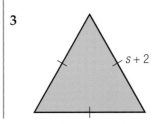

4

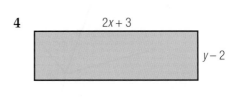

➡

5

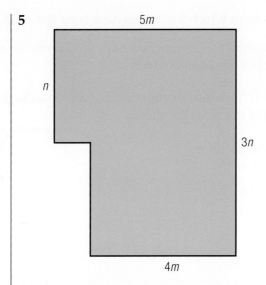

For questions 6–10, write an expression for the total of the angles around the point.

6

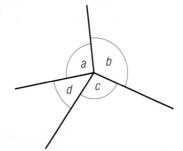

7

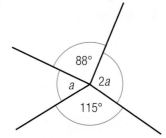

8

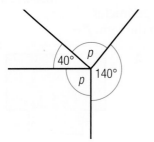

9

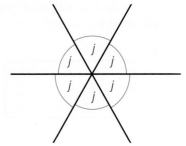

10

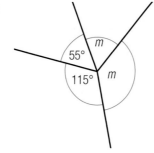

Expressions with brackets

The area of a rectangle is found by multiplying its length by its width.
  We can write an expression for the area of this shape by using brackets.

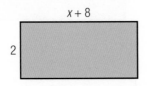

The rectangle can be split
in two as shown.

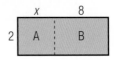

The area of A can be expressed as $2x$.
The area of B can be expressed as 16.
The total area of the rectangle is $2x + 16$.
The area of the rectangle can also be expressed using brackets as $2(x + 8)$.
Therefore
$$2(x + 8) = 2x + 16.$$

Remember that, to expand brackets, you multiply the terms inside the brackets
by the term outside. So with $2(x + 8)$, the 2 multiplies both the x and the 8:

$$2(x + 8) = 2 \times x + 2 \times 8$$
$$= 2x + 16$$

EXERCISE 2.2A

For each of the following rectangles:
a) write an expression for the area, using brackets
b) expand your expressions in part a) by multiplying out the brackets
c) derive a formula for the area in the form $A = ...$

1

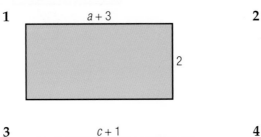

2

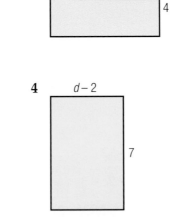

3

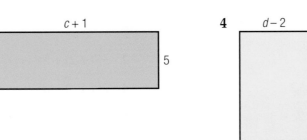

4

→

5

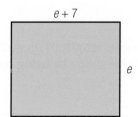

$e + 7$

e

6

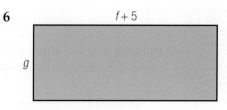

$f + 5$

g

7

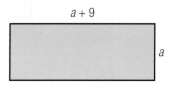

$a + 9$

a

8

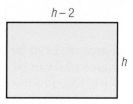

$h - 2$

h

9

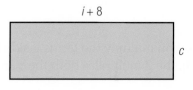

$i + 8$

c

10

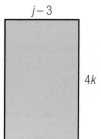

$j - 3$

$4k$

11

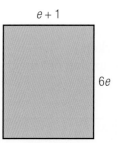

$e + 1$

$6e$

12

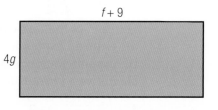

$f + 9$

$4g$

EXERCISE 2.2B

Expand the brackets in these expressions and simplify your answer where possible.

1 $3(a + 2)$

2 $3(b + 2) + 5$

3 $5(c - 8) + 12$

4 $7(d - 9) - d$

5 $3(e + 5) + 2e - 3$

6 $2(f - 2) + 3(f - 1)$

7 $4f(2f - 3) + 5f(3f - 2)$

8 $-2g(h + 4) - 3(h - 2)$

9 $5h(2i + 3) - 7(i - 1)$

10 $-3j(4 + 3j) - 2(j - 7)$

3 Congruency and properties of two-dimensional shapes

- ◆ Know that if two 2-D shapes are congruent, corresponding sides and angles are equal.
- ◆ Classify quadrilaterals according to their properties, including diagonal properties.
- ◆ Identify all the symmetries of 2-D shapes.

Congruency

You saw in Student's Book 1 that shapes can undergo different types of transformation. The transformations studied there included **reflection**, **rotation** and **translation**. In each case, the original shape (the **object**) was mapped to a new position (the **image**). An example of each of these types of transformations is shown below.

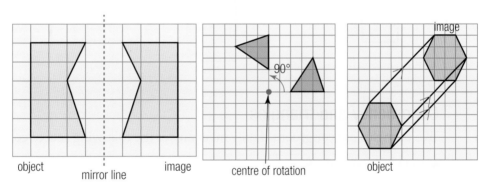

object   mirror line   image   centre of rotation   object

In each case, the object is the same size and shape as the image. We say that they are **congruent**.

Two shapes are congruent if they are exactly the same shape and size.

Although the L-shapes below have undergone rotations and reflections, they are all congruent because they are exactly the same shape and size as each other.

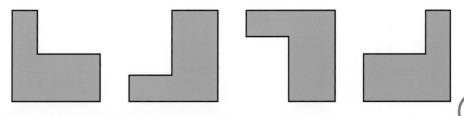

1 Determine which of these shapes are congruent to shape A.

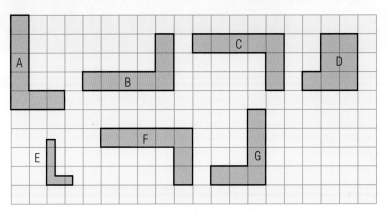

2 Shapes X and Y are congruent. Match up each side on shape X with the corresponding side on shape Y.

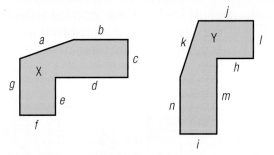

Congruency and triangles

Two triangles are congruent if they meet any of the following sets of conditions.

- Side, side, side (SSS)
  If all three sides of a triangle are the same length as the three sides of another triangle, then the two triangles are congruent. For example,

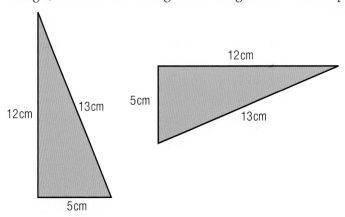

- Side, angle, side (SAS)
  If two sides and the included angle (the angle between the two sides) of both triangles are the same, then the two triangles are congruent. For example,

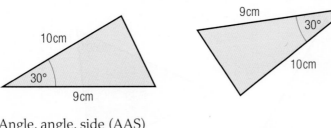

- Angle, angle, side (AAS)
  If two angles and a corresponding side of both triangles are equal, then the two triangles are congruent. For example,

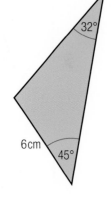

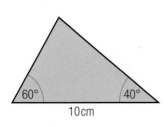
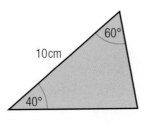

- Angle, side, angle (ASA)
  If two angles and the included side of both triangles are equal, then the two triangles are congruent. For example,

- Right angle, hypotenuse, side (RHS)
  If the hypotenuse (the side opposite the right angle, which is also the longest side) and one other side of a right-angled triangle are the same as those of another right-angled triangle, then the two triangles are congruent. For example,

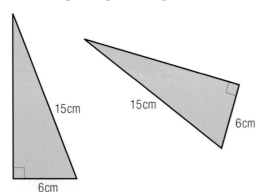

EXERCISE 3.1B

From the information given, determine which of the following pairs of triangles *must* be congruent. Give reasons for your answers.

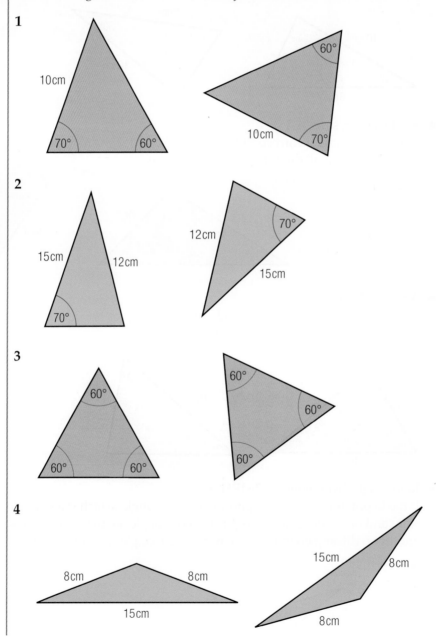

1

10cm

70° 60°

60°

10cm 70°

2

15cm 12cm

70°

12cm

70°

15cm

3

60°

60° 60°

60°

60°

60°

4

8cm 8cm

15cm

15cm 8cm

8cm

Properties of quadrilaterals

A **quadrilateral** is any closed two-dimensional shape with four straight sides.
For example,

These three shapes are all quadrilaterals, but they have different properties.
One has two pairs of parallel sides; another has only one pair of parallel sides.
The third has one pair of opposite angles that are equal.

Quadrilaterals can therefore be sub-divided into further groups with different
properties.

One way of sorting quadrilaterals is to use the flowchart below.

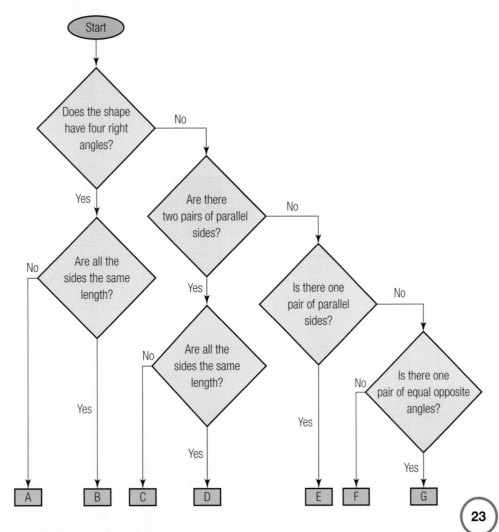

EXERCISE 3.2

1 Use the flowchart on page 23 to sort the following quadrilaterals.
Which box (A, B, C, etc.) does each of them fit into?

a)

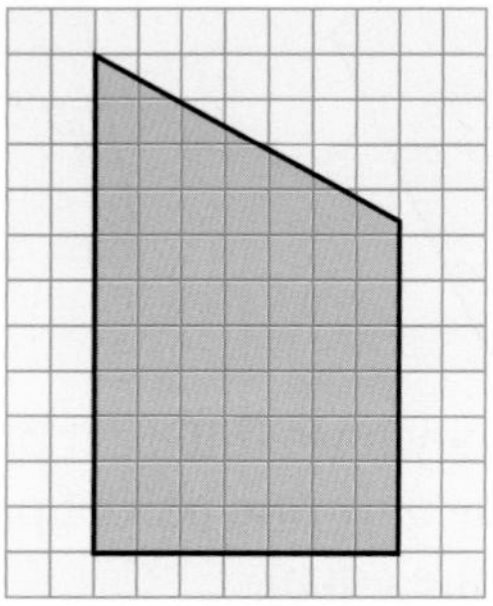

b)

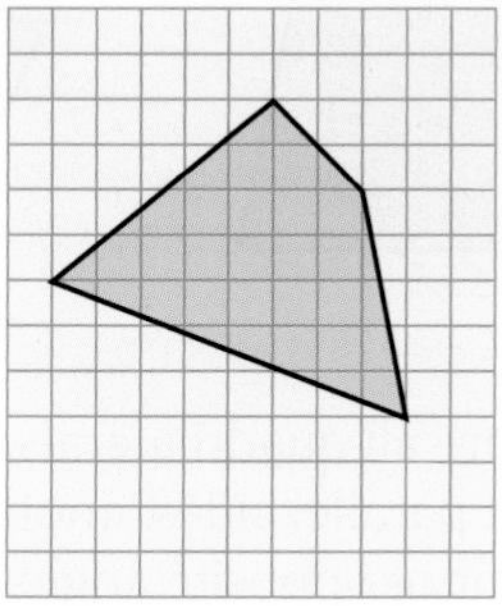

c)

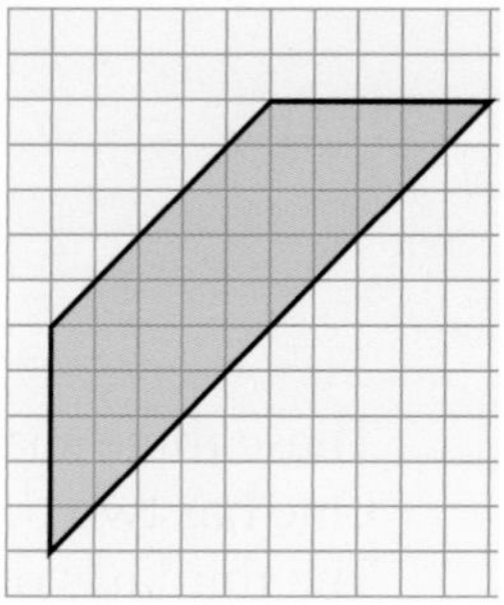

d)

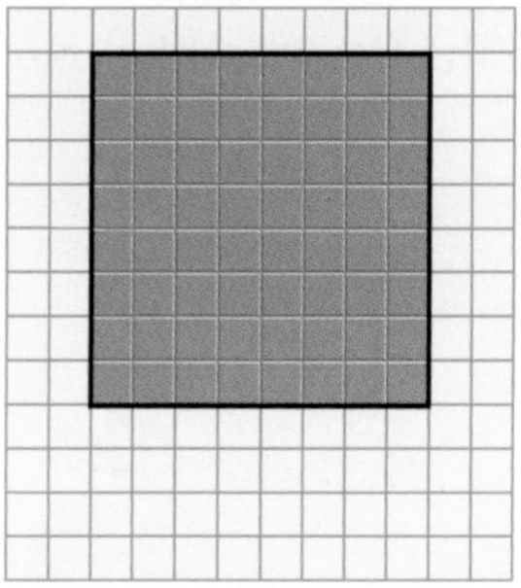

e)

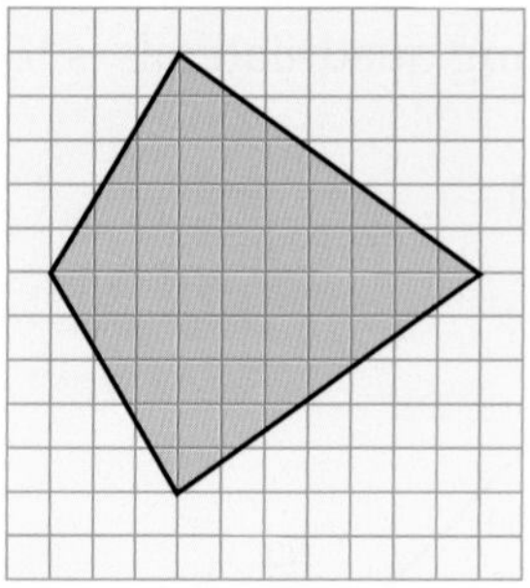

f)

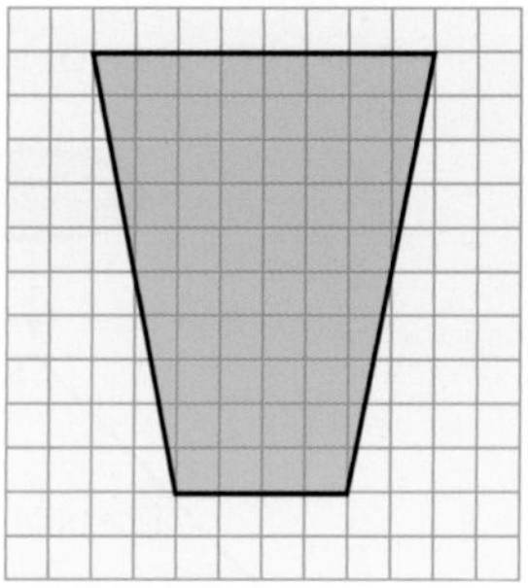

g)

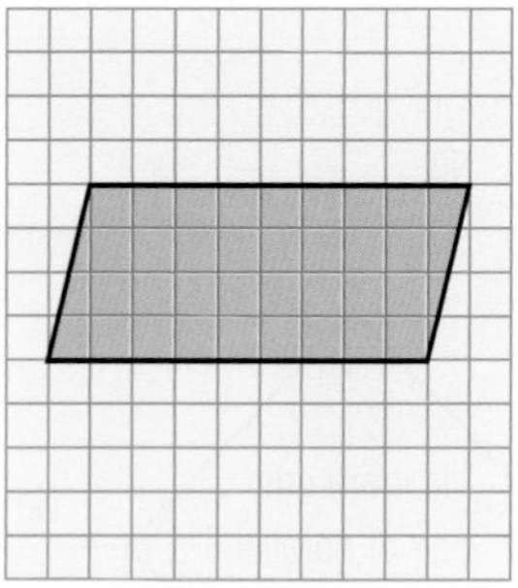

h)

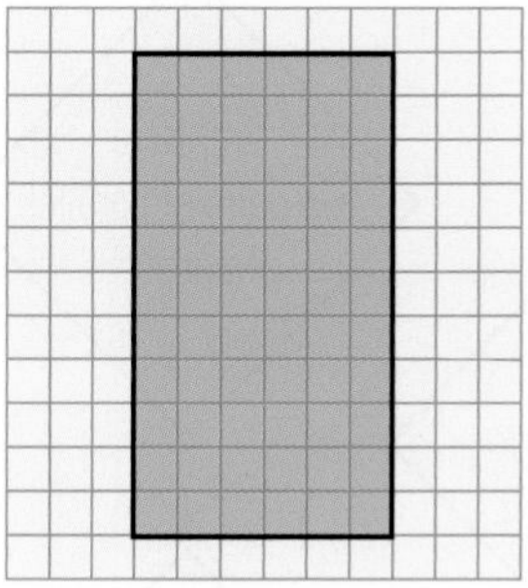

i)

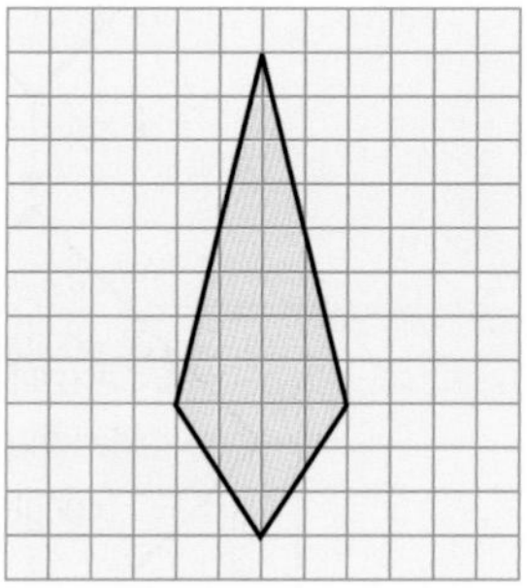

j)

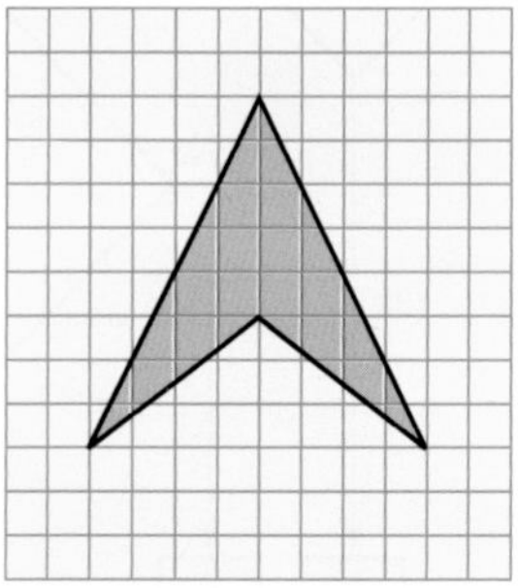

k)

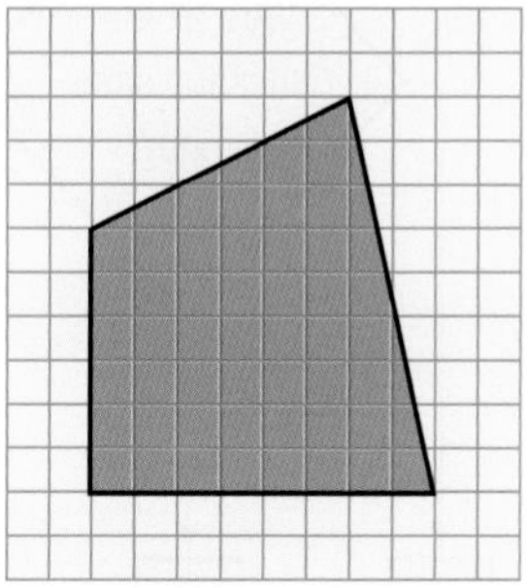

l)

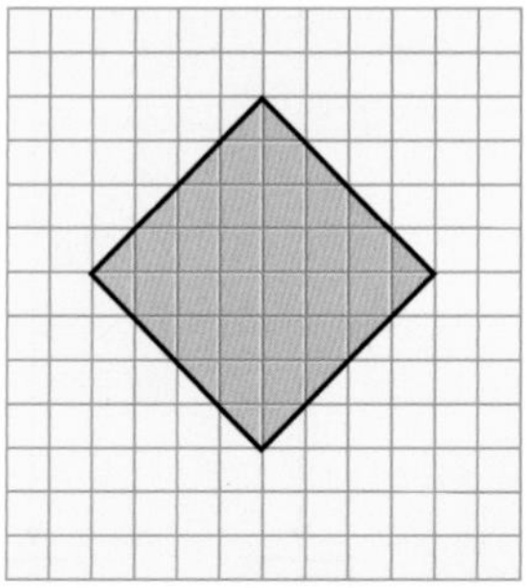

m) 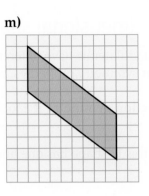   **n)** 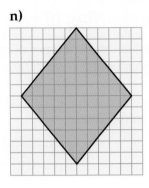   **o)**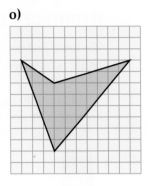

2 What special name is given to the quadrilaterals in each of these boxes on the flowchart on page 23?

a) box A   **b)** box B   **c)** box C   **d)** box D

e) box E   **f)** box F   **g)** box G

3 Copy and complete this table of the side and angle properties of different types of quadrilaterals.

	Square	Rectangle	Rhombus	Parallelogram	Trapezium	Kite
All sides equal in length	Yes					
All angles equal						
Opposite sides equal in length		Yes				
Two pairs of opposite sides parallel						
Two pairs of opposite angles equal						
One pair of opposite angles equal						
One pair of opposite sides parallel						
Diagonals equal in length						
Diagonals intersect at right angles						

Symmetry properties of two-dimensional shapes

We have just seen that different types of quadrilaterals have different side and angle properties. Shapes also have different symmetry properties, both reflection and rotation.

You already know that a shape has **reflection symmetry** if it looks the same on both sides of a mirror line.

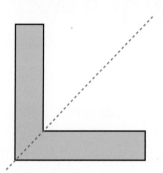

For example, this L-shape has one line of reflection symmetry.

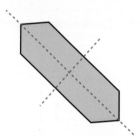

This irregular hexagon has two lines of reflection symmetry.

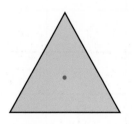

A shape has **rotational symmetry** if, during one complete revolution of 360° about the centre of rotation, it looks the same as the shape in its original position.

For example, this equilateral triangle has rotational symmetry of order 3, as in one complete rotation it looks the same *three* times.

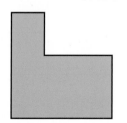

All shapes have rotational symmetry of at least order 1, because *any* shape will look the same after a full rotation of 360°. So a shape which only has rotational symmetry of order 1 is considered *not* to have rotational symmetry.

This shape looks the same only once in a full rotation, so it is not classed as having rotational symmetry.

EXERCISE 3.3

1   Copy and complete this table of the symmetry properties of different types of shapes.

Shape		Number of lines of symmetry	Order of rotational symmetry
Square			
Rectangle			
Rhombus			
Parallelogram			
Isosceles trapezium			
Kite			
Equilateral triangle			
Isosceles triangle			
Regular pentagon			
Regular hexagon			
Circle			

2 For each of these capital letters, write down:
    (i) the number of lines of reflection symmetry
    (ii) the order of rotational symmetry.

a) A   **b)** B   **c)** E   **d)** H

e) I   **f)** N   **g)** S   **h)** Z

3 Copy each of these diagrams on to squared paper.
Draw in additional lines so that the final shape has the symmetry stated.

a)

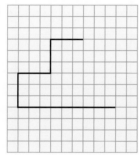

1 line of reflection symmetry
Rotational symmetry of order 1

b)

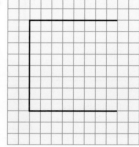

4 lines of reflection symmetry
Rotational symmetry of order 4

c)

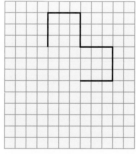

4 lines of reflection symmetry
Rotational symmetry of order 4

d)

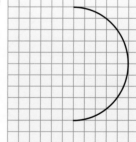

1 line of reflection symmetry
Rotational symmetry of order 1

e)

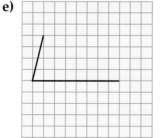

0 lines of reflection symmetry
Rotational symmetry of order 2

f)

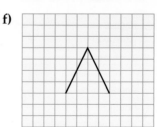

2 lines of reflection symmetry
Rotational symmetry of order 2

4 Make four copies of this 4 × 4 grid.

Shade in squares so that the final shape has:
a) 4 lines of reflection symmetry and rotational symmetry of order 4
b) 0 lines of reflection symmetry and rotational symmetry of order 4
c) 2 lines of reflection symmetry and rotational symmetry of order 2
d) 0 lines of reflection symmetry and rotational symmetry of order 2.

4 Measures and motion

◆ Choose suitable units of measurement to estimate, measure, calculate and solve problems in a range of contexts, including units of mass, length, area, volume or capacity.
◆ Know that distances in the USA, the UK and some other countries are measured in miles, and that one kilometre is about $\frac{5}{8}$ of a mile.
◆ Draw and interpret graphs in real-life contexts involving more than one component.

Metrology is the science of measures. The word comes from the Greek words 'metron' meaning measure and 'logos' meaning study. Do not confuse it with meteorology, which is the study of weather.

The earliest written records of measures come from Mesopotamia, about 4000 BCE. Their system of measures had symbols for measuring length, distance, area, volume, mass and time, and was very similar to our system. Our units of time as different fractions of a day are directly derived from theirs. Because the unit of length is related to the length of a pendulum with a one-second swing in both systems, the other units are closely related too.

> *If you are interested you can find out more about early measures on the internet.*

The metric system

The most widely used system of measurement in the world today is the **metric system**. Some countries, including the USA and the UK, also use an earlier system called the **imperial system**.

The metric system uses a number of units for length. They are:
   kilometre (km), metre (m), centimetre (cm) and millimetre (mm)

The units for mass are:
   tonne (t), kilogram (kg), gram (g) and milligram (mg)

The units for capacity are:
   litre (*l*) and millilitre (m*l*)

> *centi comes from the Latin 'centum' meaning hundred,*
> *milli comes from the Latin 'mille' meaning thousand,*
> *kilo comes from the Greek 'khilioi' meaning thousand.*

EXERCISE 4.1A

Copy and complete these sentences.

1 a) There are _____ millimetres in 4 metres.

   b) There are _____ centimetres in 3 kilometres.

   c) There are _____ grams in 5 kilograms.

   d) 2 grams is _____ part of 2 kilograms.

   e) There are _____ millilitres in 7 litres.

   f) There are _____ kg in 8 tonnes.

2 Which of these units would you use to measure each of the following?

   mm   cm   m   km   mg   g   kg   tonne   m*l*   litre

   a) the width of your foot
   b) the amount of water in a bottle
   c) the mass of a plane
   d) the capacity of the fuel tank of a truck
   e) the length of your thumbnail

3 Write an estimate for each of the following using a sensible unit.
   a) the capacity of a large bottle of water
   b) the distance to the nearest capital city
   c) the mass of a melon
   d) the width of the Atlantic Ocean
   e) the distance to the Sun

✪ Units of area and volume

We can convert between different units of area.

1 cm = 10 mm, so
$$1\,cm^2 = 10\,mm \times 10\,mm = 100\,mm^2$$

Similarly, 1 m = 100 cm, so
$$1\,m^2 = 100\,cm \times 100\,cm = 10\,000\,cm^2$$

and 1 m = 1000 mm, so
$$1\,m^2 = 1000\,mm \times 1000\,mm = 1\,000\,000\,mm^2$$

EXERCISE 4.1B

1 Copy and complete the following.

   a) $5\,cm^2 =$ _____ mm^2 b) $8\,m^2 =$ _____ cm^2

   c) _____ $m^2 = 7\,500\,000\,mm^2$ d) $64\,000\,cm^2 =$ _____ m^2

   e) _____ $cm^2 = 5600\,mm^2$

→

2 Write an estimate for each of the following using a sensible unit.
   a) the area of a football field   **b)** the area of a stamp
   c) the volume of a shoe box   **d)** the volume of a house
   e) the area of a city

The transport of goods and energy sources around the world

Crude oil (unrefined oil), natural gas and chemicals are moved around the world in very large tankers. The biggest types are called very large crude carriers (VLCCs) or ultra large crude carriers (ULCCs). A VLCC carries about 300 000 tonnes or 300 million litres, and a ULCC about 500 000 tonnes or 500 million litres.

You do not need to remember the detailed information in this section.

Manufactured goods are often carried in standard-sized containers by train or truck to ports, where they are loaded on to container ships for transport around the world.

You may wish to talk about the advantages and disadvantages of having ships with such large quantities of dangerous cargo sailing round the world.

Containers were first used in the USA and had a size of about 2.4 m by 2.4 m by 6 m. In imperial units, their length was 20 feet (1 foot is about 30 cm). Most modern containers are bigger than this (why?) but their capacities are given in 'twenty-foot equivalent units' or TEUs.

Most container ships carry between 2000 and 8000 TEUs, stacked up six or seven containers high. Big container ships carry about 15 000 TEUs and are about 300 m long and up to 60 m wide. There are at least 17 million containers in use around the world today.

EXERCISE 4.1C

Answer the following questions about oil tankers and container ships.

1 A VLCC carries 250 000 tonnes of oil in 20 self-contained tanks.
   How much oil is in one tank?

2 A 15 000 TEU ship measures 300 m by 60 m.
   How many football fields long is it?

3 5000 containers are stacked 20 wide and 50 long on a ship.
   How many containers high are they stacked?

4 If 17 million containers each 6 m long were placed end to end, would they reach to the Moon?

The Moon is 380 000 km away.

5 A standard container measures 2.4 m by 2.4 m by 6 m. Multiply the dimensions to work out its volume.

6 Use your answer to question 5 to work out the volume carried by a 12 000 TEU ship.

7 **a)** How many litres are there in 1 cubic metre of liquid?
b) How many litres would fit into a standard TEU?

8 A loaded ULCC has a mass of 400 000 tonnes. Convert this mass to kilograms.

9 How many TEUs would fit along the length of a ship 240 m long?

10 It costs about $8000 to send a single TEU container from China to the USA. How much would it cost to send 12 000 TEUs?

Imperial units

In the UK, the USA and some other countries, feet, yards and miles are used as measures of distance.

$$3 \text{ feet} = 1 \text{ yard} \quad \text{and} \quad 1760 \text{ yards} = 1 \text{ mile}$$

The mile was originally 1000 paces of a Roman legionary.

In many countries, the more mathematically logical metric system is used. The metric system and the imperial system are totally different, and conversion between them is only approximate. Roughly,

1 metre = 1.093 613 298 yards, or about 1.1 yards.
1 yard = 0.9144 m, or about 0.9 m.
1 km = 0.621 371 192 237 mile, or about 0.6 mile or $\frac{5}{8}$ mile.
1 mile = 1.609 34 km, or about 1.6 km or $\frac{8}{5}$ km.

The only conversion between imperial and metric units that you need to remember is that 1 km is about $\frac{5}{8}$ mile.

Worked example

Convert 320 km into miles.
$$320 \times \frac{5}{8} = 40 \times 5 = 200$$
320 km is about 200 miles.

EXERCISE 4.2A

Convert each length or distance into the units shown in brackets.
Use the conversions $1\,km = \frac{5}{8}$ mile and 1 mile $= \frac{8}{5}\,km$ and give your answer to one decimal place.

1 2.2 miles (km)   **2** 800 m (yards)

3 660 feet (yards)   **4** 660 feet (m)

5 5000 m (miles)   **6** 400 m (yards)

7 5 feet (cm)   **8** 10 000 miles (km)

9 7.6 km (miles)   **10** 7 miles (yards)

EXERCISE 4.2B

1 A plane is flying at 39 000 feet. What is the height in metres?

2 A man is 6 feet tall. What is his height in metres?

3 Mount Everest is 29 102 feet high. What is the height in kilometres?

4 The distance from London to Boston is 2860 miles. What is the distance in kilometres?

5 A marathon run is 26 miles 365 yards. What is the distance in kilometres?

6 An Olympic long jumper jumped 8.7 feet. What is the length in metres?

7 A discus is thrown 82.4 metres. What is the distance in feet?

8 A football field is 110 metres long. What is the length in yards?

9 Running tracks used to be 440 yards around. What is the distance in metres?

10 The Sun is 93 million miles away. What is the distance in kilometres?

Travel graphs

You already know that the motion of an object can be shown on a distance–time graph. If an object is travelling at a constant speed, the distance–time graph is a straight line. For example, the graph on the right.

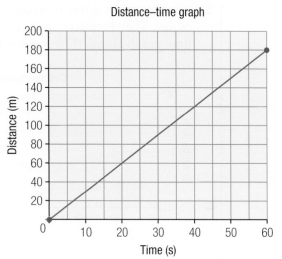

Distance–time graph

From the graph it can be seen that the object has moved 180 m in 60 s. Dividing by 60 shows that this means it moves 3 m in each second, which is a speed of 3 m/s.

EXERCISE 4.3

1 This distance–time graph shows the journeys of two people, A and B. Person A starts from his home. Person B is 10 km away when this happens.

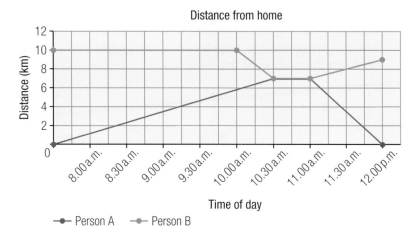

Distance from home

━●━ Person A   ━●━ Person B

a) What time does person A set off?
b) What time does person B set off?
c) What time do they meet?
d) At what speed was person A travelling before he met person B?
e) At what speed was person B travelling between 10.00 a.m. and 10.30 a.m.?
f) Who was travelling more quickly between 11.00 a.m. and 12 noon? Justify your answer without calculating their actual speeds.

2 A cyclist and a driver both set off from the same place but at different times of day. They headed to the same destination, 25 km away. This distance–time graph shows their motion during their journeys.

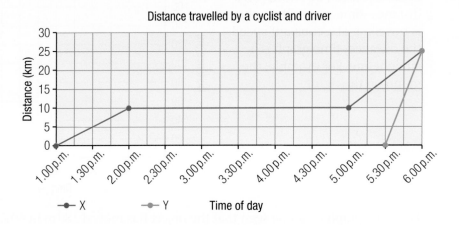

Distance travelled by a cyclist and driver

a) Which graph, X or Y, is most likely to show the cyclist's journey? Justify your answer.

b) For how long did person X stop?

c) What was the speed of person X in the first hour?

d) What was the speed of person X in the final hour?

e) What was the speed of person Y during their journey?

f) Using your answer to part **e)**, calculate how far person Y had travelled by 5.40p.m.

3 A distance–time graph is plotted to represent a train's journey. Explain, giving reasons, which two of the graphs below cannot possibly represent the motion of the train.

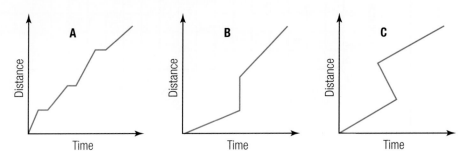

4 Here is a description of a woman's walk.
   ● She sets off from home at 8.00a.m. and walks at a constant speed of 5 km/h.
   ● She stops at 9.00a.m. for a half-hour rest.
   ● After her rest she walks a further 5 km at a constant speed, stopping again at 11.00a.m.
   ● At 11.00a.m. she stops for one hour before setting off again at a constant speed of 6 km/h.
   ● She arrives at her destination at 1.30p.m.

   a) Copy the axes below and plot a distance–time graph to show the woman's trip.

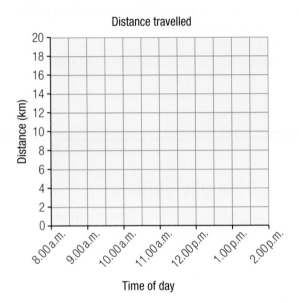

   b) Her husband starts the same trip at 11.00a.m. on his bicycle. He travels at a constant speed until he reaches the same destination at 1.00p.m. Plot his motion on the same graph.
   c) Use your graph to deduce the approximate time at which he overtook his wife.
   d) Approximately how far from home was he when he overtook his wife?

5 Collecting and displaying data

◆ Know the difference between discrete and continuous data.
◆ Identify and collect data to answer a question; select the method of collection, sample size and degree of accuracy needed for measurements.
◆ Construct and use:
  – frequency tables with given equal class intervals to gather continuous data
  – two-way tables to record discrete data.
◆ Draw, and interpret:
  – frequency diagrams for discrete and continuous data
  – pie charts
  – simple line graphs for time series
  – stem-and-leaf diagrams.

Discrete and continuous data

Pieces of information are often called **data**. **Quantitative data** – that is, data that can be measured – falls into two categories. These are discrete data and continuous data.

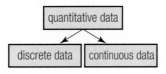

It is important to understand the difference between the two types, as the type of data collected often affects the types of graphs that can be drawn to represent it and the calculations that can be carried out.

Discrete data can only take specific values. For example, a survey to find the numbers of students in different classes can only produce values that are whole numbers. 30 students in a class would be a possible data value but 30.2 would not.

Not all data is restricted to specific values. For example, if data is collected about a sprinter's 100 m running time, a result of 10.2 seconds may be collected. But this result is only accurate to one decimal place. A more precise stopwatch may give the time as 10.23 seconds, but this in itself is only accurate to two decimal places.

Even more accurate timings may give the result as:

10.228 seconds	(to three decimal places)
10.2284 seconds	(to four decimal places)
10.228 39 seconds	(to five decimal places)

and so on.

Data that can take *any* value (usually within a range) is known as **continuous data**. The timing of an event is an example of continuous data.

EXERCISE 5.1

Decide which of the following types of data are discrete and which are continuous.

1 The mass of a baby (kg)

2 The number of people attending a concert

3 The shoe size of students in your class

4 The temperature at midday (°C)

5 The speed of cars passing the school (km/h)

6 The wingspan of a species of butterfly (mm)

7 The age of children at a party

8 The volume of water in a drinking bottle (cm³)

9 The number of pages in a book

10 The height of students in a class (cm)

Collecting data

Data is often collected in response to a problem. For example, your school canteen may wish to know what sort of food to sell. An athletics club may want to know which athletes perform consistently well. Your teacher may want to find out which topics to focus on for revision. In all these cases, for the answers to be of any use and valid, the method of data collection must be planned properly. This will include deciding how many people are going to be included in the survey. This is known as the **sample size**.

One method of collecting data is to **interview** people. The interviewer asks questions and writes down the answers given.

Q Discuss with other students the likely advantages and disadvantages of using this type of data collection.

Another method is to use **questionnaires**. A questionnaire is a printed list of questions which people answer, usually on their own without any help.

> **Q** Discuss the likely advantages and disadvantages of using this method of data collection.

EXERCISE 5.2

1 A school canteen wishes to know what sort of food to sell to students. It carries out interviews with a number of students to find out their opinions. Here is the transcript of the interviewer's conversation with one of the students.

> *Interviewer:* Hello. The school is trying to find out what sort of food it should sell to students. Can you tell me the sorts of foods you like and whether you would consider eating school food?
>
> *Student:* Hi. At the moment I don't eat school food very often. I usually bring in my own packed lunch although sometimes, if I forget my packed lunch or if my friends are all going to the canteen, then I will eat school food. When I do buy school food, I try not to spend too much, usually only about $1 or $2, but if I've had sport in the morning then I'll be really hungry and probably spend more. I like most foods, like pasta, pizza and curry, but wouldn't want to eat it every day.

a) What problems will the interviewer have when analysing this answer?
b) What is wrong with the question asked by the interviewer?
c) If you were the interviewer, what would your first question have been?
d) The interview lasts 20 minutes. Assuming all the questions are answered properly, give one of the main advantages of this method of data collection.
e) The interviewer interviews 20 students in total. Give one of the main disadvantages of this method of data collection.

2 The school also gives out the following questionnaire to the students.

> *Please tick the correct box for each question.*
>
> ● What year are you in?
>   Year 7 ☐   Year 8 ☐   Year 9 ☐   Year 10 ☐   Year 11 ☐
>
> ● What gender are you?
>   Male ☐   Female ☐

- On average, how many times a week do you eat in the school canteen?

  Never ☐   Once ☐   Twice ☐   3 times ☐

  4 times ☐   Every day ☐

- If you have eaten in the canteen, how would you rate the food?

  Excellent ☐   Good ☐   Satisfactory ☐   Poor ☐

- What food would you like to see on sale in the canteen?

  (*Tick more than one box if needed.*)

  Pizza ☐   Pasta ☐   Chicken ☐   Curry ☐   Fish ☐

  Vegetarian ☐   Salad ☐   Fruit ☐   Other ☐

- How much would you be prepared to pay for a meal in the canteen?

  Less than $2 ☐   Between $2 and $4 ☐   More than $4 ☐

a) Give two benefits of using the questionnaire above. Justify your choices.

b) Give two drawbacks of using the questionnaire. Justify your choices.

c) If you were designing the questionnaire, what additional questions would you ask?

d) The questionnaire is given out to 20 students. Give one criticism of this. Justify your answer.

e) What might be a good sample size for this questionnaire? Justify your answer.

You will have seen that both methods of data collection have advantages and disadvantages. Which method is chosen depends on several factors. The following table highlights the main advantages and disadvantages of the two methods.

	Interview	Questionnaire
Advantages	Detailed answers can be given Interviewer can clarify any misunderstandings Interviews produce a higher response rate Personal Interviewer can pick up on body language or different tone of voice	Can get the opinions of a lot of people, i.e. sample size is likely to be larger Relatively cheap to carry out Relatively quick to fill in Easy to analyse responses Format is familiar to most people Can be used for sensitive topics People have time to think about their answers
Disadvantages	Needs a skilled interviewer so that questions are not biased and so that respondent is relaxed Time consuming and therefore expensive to do Cannot be used for large numbers of people, i.e. sample size is likely to be smaller	Not suitable for complex questions Impersonal Some people don't bother returning the questionnaire Those who return the questionnaire may be interested in the topic, so the responses may be biased Questions may be misunderstood Certain questions can be ignored

Displaying data

Once the data has been collected, it can be displayed in many ways.
The methods available will depend on the type of data collected.

Two-way tables

Two-way tables can be used
when data is split into two
main categories.

For example, this two-way
table shows the numbers of
girls and boys in each of
Years 7–11 in a school.

		Year				
		7	8	9	10	11
Gender	Girls	25	31	19	34	37
	Boys	20	32	23	30	40

The two main categories here are year group and gender, but each of these
categories has got sub-divisions. The information can be read off fairly easily.
From the table we can see that there are 32 boys in Year 8. The total number of
students in Year 11 can be calculated as 77.

EXERCISE 5.3A

This two-way table shows the favourite subjects of 100 boys and girls.

		Subject				
		Maths	Science	Sport	Languages	Other
Gender	Boys	12	6	17	7	2
	Girls	21	12	6	14	3

a) Which is the most popular subject amongst the girls?
b) Which is the most popular subject amongst the boys?
c) How many girls chose science as their favourite subject?
d) How many students chose languages as their favourite subject?
e) How many girls were included in the survey?

Frequency tables and diagrams

Frequency tables are a popular way of displaying data. If the data is discrete,
then the information in the table can be displayed using a **bar chart**.
For example, the frequency table and bar chart on page 43 show the number of
pets in each house in a particular street.

Number of pets	Frequency
0	12
1	15
2	10
3	4
4	1
more than 4	2

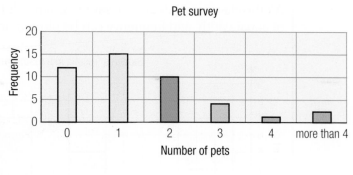

Histograms

A histogram displays the frequency of either continuous or grouped discrete data in the form of bars. There are several important features of a histogram that distinguish it from a frequency diagram:

- the bars are joined together
- the bars *can* be of varying width
- the frequency of the data is represented by the area of the bar and not the height. In most cases, the bars are of equal width, and as the area is directly proportional to the height of the bar *the height is usually used as the measure of frequency.*

Worked example

This table shows the marks out of 100 in a maths test for a class of 32 students. Draw a histogram to represent this data.

Score	Frequency
1–10	0
11–20	0
21–30	1
31–40	2
41–50	5
51–60	8
61–70	7
71–80	6
81–90	2
91–100	1

All the class intervals are the same. As a result the bars of the histogram will be of equal width, and frequency can be plotted on the vertical axis.

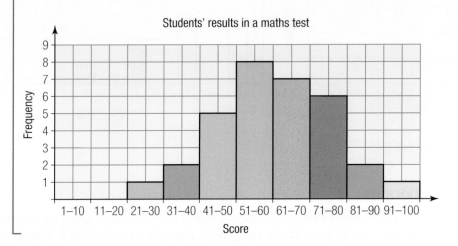

In the worked example above, groups of 10 marks were used. The group size that is chosen will affect the shape of the graph. If larger groups are used, accuracy is lost as each group will contain a lot of data. For example,

Score	Frequency
1–50	8
51–100	24

However, groups that are too small, although more accurate, may make the graph difficult to analyse as most groups will contain very little data. For example,

Score	Frequency	Score	Frequency
1–5	0	6–10	0
11–15	0	16–20	0
21–25	0	26–30	1
31–35	1	36–40	1
41–45	2	46–50	3
51–55	4	56–60	4
61–65	4	66–70	3
71–75	3	76–80	3
81–85	1	86–90	1
91–95	1	96–100	0

EXERCISE 5.3B

1 The numbers of litres of milk consumed in a group of 150 houses are shown in the table.

Number of litres	1	2	3	4	5	6
Frequency	27	54	34	16	15	4

Show this information on a frequency diagram.

2 This data records the numbers of oranges collected from 40 trees.

45	67	25	54	80	21	23	8	100	101
123	137	107	56	56	36	7	34	45	82
51	35	139	8	122	107	13	49	62	93
131	26	87	17	134	38	96	52	8	123

a) Make a grouped frequency table with class intervals 0–19, 20–39, 40–59, etc.

b) Illustrate the data on a histogram.

3 A large firm records the number of computer repairs carried out each day over a 31-day period. The results are shown below.

16	37	43	62	52	19	43	38	23	17	9
47	64	46	43	16	48	16	38	27	53	
44	34	25	52	39	39	18	15	12	8	

a) Make a grouped frequency table with class intervals 0–9, 10–19, 20–29, etc.
b) Illustrate the data on a histogram.

4 The masses of 50 rugby players attending a tournament are recorded in this grouped frequency table.

Illustrate this information on a histogram.

Mass (kg)	Frequency
70–	3
80–	7
90–	10
100–	20
110–	7
$120 \leqslant M < 130$	3

'70 –' means $70 \leqslant M < 80$ (that is, from 70 kg up to but not including 80 kg).

→

5 This table shows the numbers of hours of television watched by a group of children over a one-month period.
Illustrate this information on a histogram.

Hours of television	Frequency
0–	5
20–	5
40–	7
60–	15
80–	6
100–120	2

6 The lengths of the right feet of 32 students in a class are measured.
The results are recorded and are shown in this grouped frequency table.
Illustrate this data on a histogram.

Length (cm)	Frequency
18–	2
20–	5
22–	10
24–	10
26–28	5

7 This table shows the distances travelled to school by a class of 32 students.
Illustrate this information on a histogram.

Distance (km)	Frequency
$0 \leqslant d < 1$	9
$1 \leqslant d < 2$	4
$2 \leqslant d < 3$	7
$3 \leqslant d < 4$	2
$4 \leqslant d < 5$	5
$5 \leqslant d < 6$	1
$6 \leqslant d < 7$	3
$7 \leqslant d < 8$	1

8 The heights of students in a class were measured. The results are shown in the table. Draw a histogram to represent this data.

Height (cm)	Frequency
145–	3
150–	0
155–	6
160–	5
165–	8
170–	1
175–	4
180–185	1

9 This data records the percentage scores of students in a maths exam.

30	47	43	58	62	73	47	59	68	51	57
64	66	70	36	60	57	83	64	61	41	58
58	72	67	88	56	58	87	70	40	57	56
64	70	48	62	73	67	69	58	80	74	59

a) Make a grouped frequency table and illustrate the results on a histogram.
b) Justify the group size you chose in part **a)**.

Pie charts

Pie charts are another popular way of displaying data. With a pie chart, each sector (slice) represents a *fraction* of the total. Its size is proportional to the frequency of that category as a fraction of the total.

For example, this table shows the numbers of different flavours of ice-creams sold, and their fractions of the total number sold.

Flavour	Frequency	Fraction of the total
Vanilla	25	$\frac{25}{100} = \frac{1}{4}$
Chocolate	50	$\frac{50}{100} = \frac{1}{2}$
Strawberry	25	$\frac{25}{100} = \frac{1}{4}$

Converting this data to a pie chart is relatively straightforward, as the circle can be split into the fractions fairly easily.

If the numbers are not so straightforward, a pie chart scale (marked in percentages) or an angle measurer or protractor (marked in degrees) must be used to construct the pie chart.

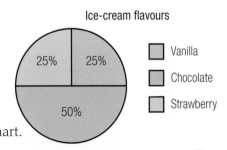

Ice-cream flavours

■ Vanilla
■ Chocolate
■ Strawberry

Worked example

The table below shows the numbers of brothers and sisters of 30 students in a class.

Number of brothers and sisters	0	1	2	3	4	5
Frequency	5	8	11	3	2	1

Show this information on a pie chart.

To express these figures as *percentages*, we need to work out what fraction each frequency is compared with the total and then multiply it by 100.

Number of brothers and sisters	Frequency	Fraction of the total	Percentage
0	5	$\frac{5}{30}$	$\frac{5}{30} \times 100 = 16.7\%$
1	8	$\frac{8}{30}$	$\frac{8}{30} \times 100 = 26.7\%$
2	11	$\frac{11}{30}$	$\frac{11}{30} \times 100 = 36.7\%$
3	3	$\frac{3}{30}$	$\frac{3}{30} \times 100 = 10\%$
4	2	$\frac{2}{30}$	$\frac{2}{30} \times 100 = 6.7\%$
5	1	$\frac{1}{30}$	$\frac{1}{30} \times 100 = 3.3\%$

The pie chart would then be drawn using a *pie chart scale*.

To express these figures as *angles*, we need to work out what fraction each frequency is compared with the total and then multiply it by 360 (as there are 360° in a full circle).

Number of brothers and sisters	Frequency	Fraction of the total	Angle
0	5	$\frac{5}{30}$	$\frac{5}{30} \times 360 = 60°$
1	8	$\frac{8}{30}$	$\frac{8}{30} \times 360 = 96°$
2	11	$\frac{11}{30}$	$\frac{11}{30} \times 360 = 132°$
3	3	$\frac{3}{30}$	$\frac{3}{30} \times 360 = 36°$
4	2	$\frac{2}{30}$	$\frac{2}{30} \times 360 = 24°$
5	1	$\frac{1}{30}$	$\frac{1}{30} \times 360 = 12°$

The pie chart would then be drawn using an *angle measurer* or *protractor*.

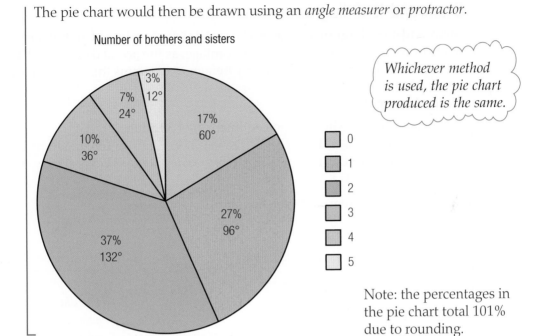

Number of brothers and sisters

Whichever method is used, the pie chart produced is the same.

Note: the percentages in the pie chart total 101% due to rounding.

EXERCISE 5.3C

1 90 students sat a maths exam. On the way out of the hall, they were asked to say whether they had found it hard, OK or easy. Here are the results.

Response	Easy	OK	Hard	No reply
Frequency	22	37	19	12

Show the results on a pie chart.

2 Two football teams have the results shown in the table.

	Total	Win	Draw	Lose
Spain	36	22	8	6
Turkey	36	21	13	2

Illustrate these on two pie charts.

3 Do a survey of 24 students in your class to see how many brothers and sisters they have. Illustrate your answers on:
a) a frequency chart
b) a pie chart.

4 Write a questionnaire to find the favourite subject of a group of students in your class and display the results on a pie chart.

Stem-and-leaf diagrams

Stem-and-leaf diagrams are a special sort of bar chart in which the 'bars' are made from the data itself. This is an advantage, as the actual data can still be seen in the diagram, whereas in many frequency diagrams this is not the case.

Worked example

This data records the heights (in centimetres) of 30 adults.

181	178	192	188	186	179	175	168	176	183
188	190	180	177	165	161	172	175	176	184
182	174	173	168	168	172	179	180	181	175

Record these in a stem-and-leaf diagram.

```
16 | 1 5 8 8 8
17 | 2 2 3 4 5 5 5 6 6 7 8 9 9
18 | 0 0 1 1 2 3 4 6 8 8
19 | 0 2
```

stem   leaves

Key
|16| 5 means 165 cm.

The diagram must have a key to explain what the stem means. If the data were 1.8, 2.7, 3.2, etc., the key would state that '|2| 7 means 2.7'.

Note that the 'leaves' on each of the 'branches' must be in order.

Calculating the mean, median and mode from a stem-and-leaf diagram

As the original data is not lost, it is possible to calculate the exact values for the mean, median and mode from a stem-and-leaf diagram.

Worked example

The stem-and-leaf diagram below shows the lengths (in centimetres) of 20 earthworms collected for a study.

```
 8 | 0 1 3
 9 | 1 2 2 2 5 8
10 | 4 6 6 6 6 9
11 | 1 2 2 3 3
```

Key
|10| 9 means 10.9 cm.

Calculate the mean, median and modal earthworm lengths.

The mean is calculated by finding the sum of all the data values and dividing by the number of values:

$$\text{mean} = \frac{8.0 + 8.1 + 8.3 + 9.1 + \cdots + 11.2 + 11.3 + 11.3}{20} = \frac{200.2}{20} = 10.0\,\text{cm}$$

The median represents the middle value when the data is arranged in order. In a stem-and-leaf diagram, the data is in order. As there are 20 data values, there is not a middle value but a middle *pair*. Here, these are the 10th and 11th values, which we can find by counting along the 'leaves':

```
 8  | 0  1  3
 9  | 1  2  2  2  5  8
10  | 4  6  6  6  6  9
11  | 1  2  2  3  3
```

They are 10.4 cm and 10.6 cm. The median is the mean of these values, i.e. 10.5 cm.

The mode is the value that occurs most often. These values are highlighted below.

```
 8  | 0  1  3
 9  | 1  2  2  2  5  8
10  | 4  6  6  6  6  9
11  | 1  2  2  3  3
```

The modal length is therefore 10.6 cm.

1 A junior weightlifter keeps a record of the maximum weights (in kilograms) he lifted in his 20 most recent competitions. The weights are:

56	58	58	55	54	50	48	56	57	52
50	56	58	58	61	60	59	58	58	53

a) Draw a stem-and-leaf diagram of the data.
b) From the stem-and-leaf diagram calculate:
    (i) the median weight lifted
    (ii) the modal weight lifted.

2 The lifetimes (in hours of continuous use) of 25 batteries of a particular brand are shown below.

36	38	42	32	35	44	47	43	42	34
42	39	40	36	38	42	43	46	29	30
50	51	38	31	42					

→

a) Draw a stem-and-leaf diagram of the data.
b) From the diagram calculate:
   (i)   the mean lifetime of the batteries
   (ii) the median lifetime
   (iii) the modal lifetime.
c) The manufacturer wants to print the average lifetime on the packaging. Which of these values are they most likely to choose?

3   The wingspans (in centimetres) of 24 adult birds of a particular species are recorded. The results are shown below.

23.8	22.1	21.9	23.6	23.9	24.2	24.2	23.5
23.5	23.6	24.2	25.0	23.8	22.8	22.9	22.5
23.5	23.7	23.4	23.9	23.5	24.0	24.2	24.8

a) Draw a stem-and-leaf diagram of the data.
b) The report from a previous study stated that the average wingspan for this species was 23.6 cm. By calculating the mean and median from the data above, comment on whether the average wingspan has changed since the previous study.

Line graphs

So far, all the data we have looked at represents values at a particular moment in time, for example the heights of students in a class or the wingspan of birds. Quite often, however, data is collected over a period of time. This is plotted as a **line graph** with time along the x axis.

Worked example

The temperature (in °C) at a ski resort is recorded every 4 hours. The table shows the results for one of the days.

Time	00.00	04.00	08.00	12.00	16.00	20.00	24.00
Temperature (°C)	−8	−11	−6	3	4	1	−5

a) Display the data as a line graph.
b) Use the graph to estimate the temperature in the resort at 10.00a.m.

a)

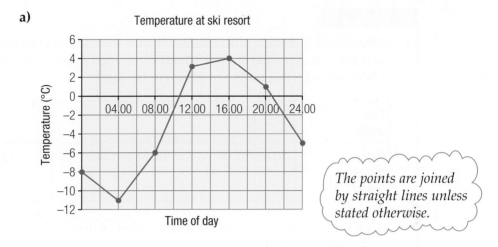

The points are joined by straight lines unless stated otherwise.

b) Although only seven temperature readings were taken, it is reasonable to assume that the temperature changed in a linear way between the readings. That is, because the temperature was −6 °C at 08.00a.m. and 3 °C at 12.00, we assume that the temperature rose steadily between the two readings.

We draw a line vertically from 10.00a.m. until it meets the graph, and then draw a horizontal line from this point to meet the temperature axis:

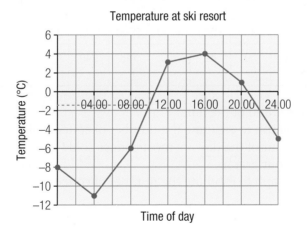

The temperature at 10.00.am. can therefore be estimated as approximately −1.5 °C.

EXERCISE 5.3E

1 A stadium is holding a music festival. When the gates are opened, the total number of people in the stadium is recorded every 20 minutes over a 3-hour period. The results are shown in the table.

Time (mins)	0	20	40	60	80	100	120	140	160	180
Total number of people	0	3000	10000	18000	22000	36000	40000	44000	45000	46000

a) Plot a line graph to show the total number of people in the stadium over the 3-hour period.
b) Use your graph to estimate the number of people in the stadium after $1\frac{1}{2}$ hours.
c) Use your graph to estimate the number of people who entered the stadium between the 50th and 90th minutes after the gates opened.

2 In a café, the number of coffees sold is recorded every hour and the total number sold since the start of the day is calculated. The café opens at 08 00. The totals are shown in the table below.

Time	09 00	10 00	11 00	12 00	13 00	14 00	15 00	16 00
Total number of coffees sold	50	82	100	148	240	275	301	313

a) Plot a line graph of the data.
b) Use your graph to estimate the number of coffees sold by 11 15.
c) In which hour of the day are most coffees sold? Explain how you can tell this from your graph.
d) Use your graph to estimate the number of coffees sold between 11 30 and 14 30.

3   A swimming pool is left to heat up over a weekend. Unfortunately,
     the thermostat does not work properly and the pool overheats.
     The temperature of the water at 0900 on Monday morning is 56 °C.
        The heater is switched off and temperature readings are taken every
     6 hours over the next three days. The results are shown below.

Day	Monday			Tuesday				Wednesday			
Time	0900	1500	2100	0300	0900	1500	2100	0300	0900	1500	2100
Temperature (°C)	56	40	32	27	23	21	20	19.5	19	18.5	18

a) Plot a line graph of the data and draw a smooth curve through the
   points.
b) Estimate the temperature of the pool at 1800 on Monday evening.
c) The pool can only be opened to the public once the temperature has
   dropped to 25 °C. Estimate the time at which the pool could have
   been opened.
d) At what time was the temperature of the pool dropping the fastest?
   Explain, with reference to your graph, how you reached your answer.

6 Calculations and mental strategies 1

◆ Recall squares to 20×20, cubes to $5 \times 5 \times 5$, and corresponding roots.
◆ Recall relationships between units of measurement.
◆ Use the order of operations, including brackets, with more complex calculations.

Mental strategies

You should already know these **square numbers**. Learn them now if you do not.

$1 \times 1 = 1$
$2 \times 2 = 4$
$3 \times 3 = 9$
$4 \times 4 = 16$
$5 \times 5 = 25$
$6 \times 6 = 36$
$7 \times 7 = 49$
$8 \times 8 = 64$
$9 \times 9 = 81$
$10 \times 10 = 100$

You may not know these bigger square numbers. You must learn these too.

$11 \times 11 = 121$
$12 \times 12 = 144$
$13 \times 13 = 169$
$14 \times 14 = 196$
$15 \times 15 = 225$
$16 \times 16 = 256$
$17 \times 17 = 289$
$18 \times 18 = 324$
$19 \times 19 = 361$
$20 \times 20 = 400$

A **cube number** is one which is obtained by multiplying a number by itself three times. The first five cube numbers are shown below. You should learn these too.

$$1 \times 1 \times 1 = 1$$
$$2 \times 2 \times 2 = 8$$
$$3 \times 3 \times 3 = 27$$
$$4 \times 4 \times 4 = 64$$
$$5 \times 5 \times 5 = 125$$

EXERCISE 6.1A

Work with a partner and ask each other the following questions. Do them in your head.

One of you asks part **a)**, the other asks part **b)**.

1	**a)** 5×5	**b)** 3×3
2	**a)** 8×8	**b)** 4×4
3	**a)** 7×7	**b)** 9×9
4	**a)** 6×6	**b)** 11×11
5	**a)** 12×12	**b)** 13×13
6	**a)** 15×15	**b)** 17×17
7	**a)** 20×20	**b)** 14×14
8	**a)** $3 \times 3 \times 3$	**b)** $4 \times 4 \times 4$
9	**a)** $5 \times 5 \times 5$	**b)** $2 \times 2 \times 2$
10	**a)** 16×16	**b)** 15×15

Converting from one metric unit to another

You should already know how to convert length, mass and capacity from one unit to another as shown below.

Length

1 km is 1000 m, so

to change from km to m, multiply by 1000
to change from m to km, divide by 1000.

Worked examples

a) Change 3.8 km to metres.
1 km = 1000 m so multiply by 1000.
$3.8 \times 1000 = 3800$ m

b) Change 7600 mm to metres.
1 m = 1000 mm so divide by 1000.
$7600 \div 1000 = 7.6$ m

Remember also that 10 mm = 1 cm.

Mass

1 tonne is 1000 kg, so
> to change from tonnes to kg, multiply by 1000
> to change from kg to tonnes, divide by 1000.

Worked examples

a) Change 0.8 tonne to kilograms.
1 tonne = 1000 kg so multiply by 1000.
$0.8 \times 1000 = 800$ kg

b) Change 4200 kg to tonnes.
1 tonne = 1000 kg so divide by 1000.
$4200 \div 1000 = 4.2$ tonnes

Capacity

1 litre is 1000 ml, so
> to change from litres to ml, multiply by 1000
> to change from ml to litres, divide by 1000.

Worked examples

a) Change 1.4 litres to millilitres.
1 litre is 1000 ml, so multiply by 1000.
$1.4 \times 1000 = 1400$ ml

b) Change 2500 ml to litres.
1 litre is 1000 ml, so divide by 1000.
$2500 \div 1000 = 2.5$ litres

EXERCISE 6.1B

Work with a partner and ask each other the following questions. Do them in your head.

One of you asks part **a)**, the other asks part **b)**.

1 Convert these to millimetres.
    a) 4 cm   **b)** 6.2 cm

2 Convert these to metres.
    a) 250 cm   **b)** 1900 cm

3 Convert these to kilometres.
    a) 2000 m   **b)** 26 000 m

4 Read and complete the sentences below.

    1 kg is 1000 g, so

    a) to change kg to g _____.
    b) to change g to kg _____.

5 Convert these to kilograms.
    a) 3 tonnes   **b)** 3.2 tonnes

6 Convert these to millilitres.
    a) 2.5 litres   **b)** 0.4 litre

7 Convert these to litres.
    a) 1400 m*l*   **b)** 5200 m*l*

8 Convert these to kilograms.
    a) 25 000 g   **b)** 74 000 g

9 Convert these to millilitres.
    a) 8.5 litres   **b)** 0.75 litre

10 Convert these to litres.
    a) 1.50 m*l*   **b)** 250 m*l*

Using a calculator

There are many different types of calculator available today: basic calculators, scientific calculators and the latest graphical calculators. But today's calculators have a long history of development.

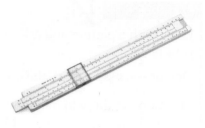

The abacus was invented between 2300 BCE and 500 BCE. It was mainly used for addition and subtraction.

The slide rule was invented in 1621. It could be used to do more difficult calculations than the abacus, although not addition or subtraction. It continued to be widely used up until the early 1970s.

The first mechanical calculator was invented by Blaise Pascal in 1642. It used a system of gears.

The first hand-held calculator appeared in 1967 as a result of the development of the integrated circuit.

However, for calculators to be properly useful, you need to know how to maximise their potential. This section is aimed at familiarising you with some of the basic operations.

The four basic operations

Worked examples

a) Using a calculator, work out the answer to this calculation.

$$15.3 + 11.8 =$$

b) Using a calculator, work out the answer to this calculation.

$$22.4 \times 10.1 =$$

The two calculations below give the same answer but are entered into the calculator in different ways.

$$5.2 - 2.3 =$$
$$5.2 + -2.3 =$$

In the first case, 2.3 is subtracted from 5.2. On a calculator this would be done using the ⊖ button.

In the second case, negative 2.3 is added to 5.2. To be able to enter a negative number into the calculator, use the 'change sign' button. On most calculators this will look like [+/−] or [(−)]. Therefore the calculation becomes:

EXERCISE 6.2A

Using a calculator, work out the answers to the following calculations.

1. **a)** $3.6 + 11.2$ **b)** $22.1 + 9.04$ **c)** $5.06 + 4.6$
   d) $91.0 + 9.01$ **e)** $13.13 + 31.31$ **f)** $9.09 + 0.01$

2. **a)** $13.6 - 2.5$ **b)** $11.4 - 0.5$ **c)** $15.04 - 30.08$
   d) $5.67 - 5.68$ **e)** $-8.1 - 3.6$ **f)** $-6.7 - 3.3$
   g) $-16 - (-4)$ **h)** $-3.72 - (-3.72)$

3. **a)** 4.6×3.7 **b)** 19.2×8.3 **c)** $5.5 \times 3.6 \times 2.2$
   d) $12.4 \div 3.1$ **e)** $7.02 \times (-5)$ **f)** $25.5 \div (-5)$
   g) $-8.1 \times (-2.3)$ **h)** $-35 \div (-3.5)$

The order of operations

Although calculations that involve several operations are written on the page from left to right, they are not always done in that order. This is because in mathematics some calculations are always carried out before others.

Worked examples

a) Use a scientific calculator to work out the answer to this calculation.
$$2 \times 4 + 5 =$$

b) Use a scientific calculator to work out the answer to this calculation.
$$2 + 4 \times 5 =$$

In the first example, doing the calculation from left to right gives the same answer as using a scientific calculator. In the second example, however, working from left to right would give an answer of 30, whilst a scientific calculator gives an answer of 22.

The reason a scientific calculator does not work the calculation out from left to right is that, in mathematics, different operations are given different priorities; by convention, some types of operations are done before others. We can see from the two examples on page 61 that multiplication is done before addition. Similarly, as subtraction is the opposite of addition, and division is the opposite of multiplication, division is done before subtraction. Therefore multiplications and divisions in a calculation take priority over additions and subtractions.

Worked examples

a) Use a scientific calculator to work out the answer to this calculation.
$$8 - 4 \div 4 =$$

The answer is 7, and not 1, because the calculator works out $4 \div 4$ first and then subtracts the answer from 8.

b) Use a scientific calculator to work out the answer to this calculation.
$$9 + 7 \times 4 \div 2 =$$

Here the multiplication and division are carried out first and then the answer is added to 9. Note: It does not matter which of multiplication or division is done first.

There will, however, be times when we will want an addition or subtraction to be done before a multiplication or division.
Consider the following calculation.
$$6 + 8 \div 2 =$$

A scientific calculator would work out the division first, giving a final answer of 10. However, if we wanted to work out $6 + 8$ first we would need to put this sum inside **brackets**. This is because brackets have the highest order of priority in any calculation, i.e. what is inside brackets is always done before any other operation. Therefore:

whilst

So far, therefore, the orders of priority in calculations is:

1 brackets

2 multiplication and/or division

3 addition and/or subtraction.

EXERCISE 6.2B

For questions 1–3, work out the answers:
(i) in your head
(ii) using a scientific calculator.

1 **a)** $12 \times 2 - 4$ **b)** $8 \times 3 + 6$
    c) $4 + 10 \times 2$ **d)** $16 - 8 \div 4$
    e) $44 - 4 \div 4$ **f)** $9 \times 6 \div 3$

2 **a)** $3 \times 2 + 4 \times 3$ **b)** $8 + 3 \times 2 - 5$
    c) $9 - 6 \div 3 + 4$ **d)** $20 \div 5 \times 2 - 8$
    e) $16 - 8 \div 8 + 3 \times 4$ **f)** $5 + 3 \times 2 \div 6 - 5$

3 **a)** $(4 + 1) \times 3$ **b)** $6 \times (8 - 5)$
    c) $(24 - 6) \div 9$ **d)** $(3 + 2) \times (12 - 5)$
    e) $(4 - 1) + 3 \times 4$ **f)** $6 \times (3 + 5) \div 8$

For questions 4–6:
(i) copy the calculation and put in any brackets that are needed to make
    it correct
(ii) check your answers using a scientific calculator.

4 **a)** $12 - 8 \times 2 = 8$ **b)** $5 \times 2 + 4 = 30$
    c) $2 \times 3 + 4 - 5 = 4$ **d)** $10 - 4 \times 3 + 3 = 36$
    e) $9 + 6 - 3 \div 2 + 4 = 10$ **f)** $9 + 6 - 3 \div 2 + 4 = 2$

5 **a)** $20 - 8 \div 2 + 6 = 22$ **b)** $20 - 8 \div 2 + 6 = 12$
    c) $20 - 8 \div 2 + 6 = 1.5$ **d)** $20 - 8 \div 2 + 6 = 10$
    e) $20 - 8 \div 2 + 6 = 19$

6 **a)** $8 + 3 \times 4 - 6 = 14$ **b)** $8 + 3 \times 4 - 6 = 38$
    c) $8 + 3 \times 4 - 6 = -22$ **d)** $8 + 3 \times 4 - 6 = 2$

Powers

Calculators have many different keys, some of which are simply more efficient
ways of carrying out ordinary calculations.
    Examples of this are the 'to the power of' buttons.

Worked examples

a) Using a calculator, work out 9×9.
    9×9 can also be written as 9^2. This is nine squared or 9 to the power of 2.
    The calculator provides an efficient way of squaring a number by using
    the $\boxed{x^2}$ key.
    Therefore 9^2 can be typed into the calculator as:
    $\boxed{9}\ \boxed{x^2}\ \boxed{=}\ \boxed{\quad 81\quad}$

b) Using a calculator, work out $6 \times 6 \times 6 \times 6$.

The calculation could be typed into the calculator as $6 \times 6 \times 6 \times 6$, but this is not efficient. $6 \times 6 \times 6 \times 6$ can also be written as 6^4, i.e. 6 to the power of 4.

On most calculators the $\boxed{y^x}$ key or the $\boxed{\wedge}$ key is the 'to the power of' or **index** key.

> The word 'index' refers to the power of a number. The plural of index is **indices**.

So 6^4 can be entered into the calculator as:

$\boxed{6}\ \boxed{y^x}\ \boxed{4}\ \boxed{=}\ \boxed{1296}$

c) Calculate 2×4^3.

In this calculation it is important to realise another priority in calculations. Powers are second in order of priority, after brackets. Therefore, in the calculation above, 4^3 is worked out before the multiplication by 2. Therefore entering the calculation into the calculator gives:

$\boxed{2}\ \boxed{\times}\ \boxed{4}\ \boxed{y^x}\ \boxed{3}\ \boxed{=}\ \boxed{128}$

Note: if we wanted to multiply the 4 by the 2 first, before raising it to the power of 3, we would need to put the 2×4 in brackets, i.e. $(2 \times 4)^3$.

d) Work out this calculation using a scientific calculator.

$$\frac{19 + 13}{2^3}$$

It is important to realise that the fraction bar means that the answer to $19 + 13$ should be worked out before being divided by 2^3. Therefore typing the following into the calculator would give an *incorrect* answer.

$\boxed{1}\ \boxed{9}\ \boxed{+}\ \boxed{1}\ \boxed{3}\ \boxed{\div}\ \boxed{2}\ \boxed{y^x}\ \boxed{3}\ \boxed{=}$

The answer would be incorrect because the order of priority of operations means that only the 13 would be divided by 2^3. Brackets must be used to ensure that the result of $19 + 13$ is divided by 2^3, i.e.

$\boxed{(}\ \boxed{1}\ \boxed{9}\ \boxed{+}\ \boxed{1}\ \boxed{3}\ \boxed{)}\ \boxed{\div}\ \boxed{2}\ \boxed{y^x}\ \boxed{3}\ \boxed{=}\ \boxed{4}$

Therefore, the order of priority in calculations is:
1 **brackets**
2 **indices**
3 **division and/or multiplication**
4 **addition and/or subtraction.**

> You can use the shorthand 'BIDMAS' to help you remember this.

EXERCISE 6.2C

Using a scientific calculator, work out the answers to the following calculations.

1 a) $\dfrac{8+4}{3}$ b) $\dfrac{36}{11-2}$ c) $\dfrac{15+6}{11-4}$

   d) $5+\dfrac{12}{4}$ e) $15-\dfrac{18}{6}$ f) $2+\dfrac{25-9}{4}$

2 a) 3^2+4 b) 8^2-3^3 c) $\dfrac{6^3}{16+2}$

   d) $\dfrac{(5+3)^2}{6-1}$ e) $\dfrac{4^3+6^2}{2^5}-3$ f) $\dfrac{(4+3)^3}{14}-24$

7 ICT, investigations and problem solving

1 Estimating angles

'It is easy to estimate the size of an acute angle. It is harder to estimate the size of an obtuse angle. It is very difficult to estimate the size of a reflex angle.'
You are going to collect and display data to see if this statement is true or false.

a) You will need three pieces of paper or card. Draw on them:
    (i) an acute angle (less than 90°)
    (ii) an obtuse angle (between 90° and 180°)
    (iii) a reflex angle (more than 180°).

    On each of them, mark clearly the angle to be estimated. For example,

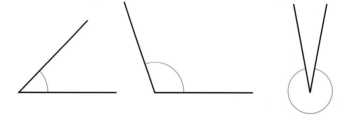

b) Explain to your class that you are going to show them three angles in turn for five seconds each, and that you will ask them to estimate the size of each angle.
c) Show each person in your class each of the angles for about five seconds and ask them for an estimate.
d) Record the responses on a piece of paper. This is called 'raw data'.
e) Design a clear table for the results.
f) Display the data using a suitable graph.
g) What conclusions can you draw from your results?
h) Suggest ways in which the experiment could be improved.
⭐ **i)** Test the following statement:
    'People become better at estimating the size of an angle if they practise.'

2 Test scores

You are probably used to sitting tests, and often the scores in tests are given as percentages. Your teacher will have a record of the scores gained by each student in your class in recent tests.

a) Obtain two sets of test scores for your class from your teacher.

Names of students are not needed – just lists of the scores.

b) Group the data in suitable intervals and then enter the data in a similar way to that shown here.

Score (%)	Frequency	
	Test 1	Test 2
30–	2	0
40–	3	0
50–	5	8
60–	8	9
70–	4	4
80–	2	2
90–100	1	2

c) Using the graphing facility of a spreadsheet program, illustrate both sets of data.

d) Write a brief report highlighting the similarities and differences between the two sets of data. In your report make reference to your graphs.

Review 1A

1 A stadium has 64 593 seats.
   a) Write this number in words.
   b) Round the number:
      (i) to the nearest thousand
      (ii) to the nearest hundred.

2 A car transporter can carry 13 cars.
   How many transporters are needed for 340 cars?

3 For each of the following rectangles:
   (i) write an expression for the area, using brackets
   (ii) expand your expressions in part **(i)** by multiplying out the brackets
   (iii) derive a formula for the area in the form $A = ...$

a)

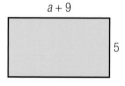
$a + 9$

5

b)

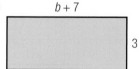
$b + 7$

3

c)

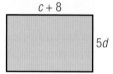
$c + 8$

$5d$

d)

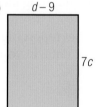
$d - 9$

$7c$

e)

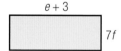
$e + 3$

$7f$

f)

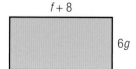
$f + 8$

$6g$

4 Expand the brackets in these expressions and simplify your answer where
   possible.
   a) $4(f - 2) + 5(f - 5)$
   b) $7(-2g - 3) + 8(3g - 2)$
   c) $-6(h + 3) - 8(h - 7)$

5 Explain whether or not these two triangles are congruent. Give reasons for your answer.

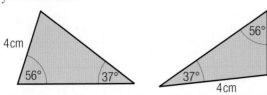

6 Write down the name of each of these quadrilaterals.

a)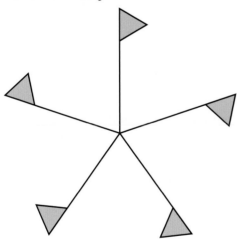

b)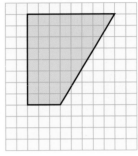

7 Look at this shape.

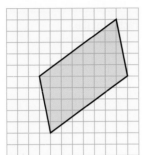

    a) Write down the number of lines of reflection symmetry.

    b) Write down the order of rotational symmetry.

8 **a)** A plane is flying at 11 887 m.
       What is the height in feet?

    b) Mount Everest is 8870 m high.
       What is the height in feet?

    c) A marathon run is about 42 km.
       What is the distance in miles?

    d) The Sun is 150 million kilometres away.
       What is the distance in miles?

> 1 metre is about 1.1 yards
> $1\,km = \frac{5}{8}\,mile$
> 1 yard = 3 feet

9   In a survey, 30 students are asked how many bedrooms their house has.
    The results are shown in this table.

Number of bedrooms	1	2	3	4	5	6
Frequency	1	8	15	5	0	1

a) The data is to be shown on a pie chart. Copy and complete the table
below.

Number of bedrooms	Frequency	Fraction of the total	Angle
1	1	$\frac{1}{30}$	$\frac{1}{30} \times 360 =$
2	8		
3			
4			
5			
6			

b) Construct a pie chart to show the data.

10 Using a calculator, work out the answers to the following calculations.

a) $3 + \dfrac{45 - 10}{5}$

b) $\dfrac{8^2}{18 - 2}$

1 A ship can carry 8500 tonnes of cargo.
How many containers, each weighing 18 tonnes, can it carry safely?

2 A baker makes loaves weighing 425 g.
How many loaves can he make from 15 kg of dough?

3 Copy and complete the following statements, writing one of the signs =, >
or < to make each statement true.

a) 8×8 _____ $4 \times 4 \times 4$ **b)** 120 cm _____ 1.21 m

c) 73 cm _____ 0.7 m   **d)** 100 cm _____ 1000 mm

e) 4.75 tonnes _____ 47 500 kg

4 For each of the following shapes:
(i) write a simplified expression for the perimeter
(ii) derive a formula for the perimeter in the form $P = ...$

a)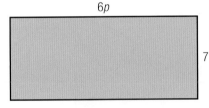

b)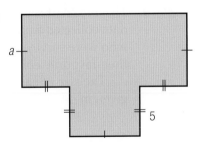

a)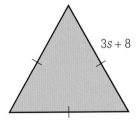

b)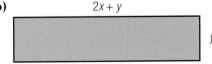

5 Expand the brackets in these expressions and simplify your answer where
possible.
a) $3(a + 2) - 2(b - 1)$
b) $3a(b + 2) + 5(2b + 5)$
c) $-5b(c - 8) - 2b(7 - 4c)$

6 Write down the name of each of these quadrilaterals.

a)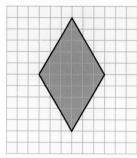

b)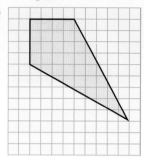

7 Look at this shape.
  a) Write down the number of lines of reflection symmetry.
  b) Write down the order of rotational symmetry.

8 **a)** A loaded ship has a mass of 155 000 tonnes. Convert this to kilograms.
  b) How many containers each 8 m long would fit along the length of a ship 174 m long?
  c) It costs about $5200 to send a single container from China to Germany. How much would it cost to send 8500 containers?

9 This pie chart represents the data collected from 60 people who were surveyed about their favourite colour.
   The size of each sector is given in degrees.

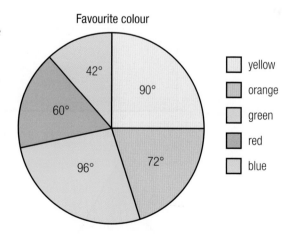

Favourite colour

42°
90°
60°
96°
72°

□ yellow
□ orange
□ green
■ red
□ blue

  a) How many degrees represent one person?
  b) How many people said yellow was their favourite colour?
  c) How many people said orange was their favourite colour?
  d) How many more people preferred green than preferred blue?

10 Copy each of these calculations and put in any brackets that are needed to make it correct.
  a) $24 - 3 \div 3 + 4 = 11$
  b) $24 - 3 \div 3 + 4 = 27$
  c) $24 - 3 \div 3 + 4 = 3$

SECTION 2

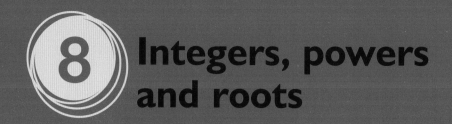

8 Integers, powers and roots

◆ Add, subtract, multiply and divide integers.
◆ Identify and use multiples, factors, common factors, highest common factors, lowest common multiples and primes; write a number in terms of its prime factors, e.g. $500 = 2^2 \times 5^3$.
◆ Calculate squares, positive and negative square roots, cubes and cube roots; use the notation $\sqrt{49}$ and $\sqrt[3]{64}$ and index notation for positive integer powers.

Integers

The set of all integers is usually shown as a double capital letter 'Z', like this:

$\mathbb{Z}$

This stands for 'Zahlen', which is the German word for numbers.

Integers are whole numbers. They can be positive, negative or zero. Examples of integers are 7, 2, −3 and −5.

Integers are shown on this number line. Left to right is the positive direction. Right to left is the negative direction.

Adding and subtracting integers

Worked examples

a) Use a number line to add (+4) and (−2).
Start at (+4) and move 2 in the negative direction.

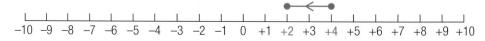

So

(+4) + (−2) = (+2)   or 2

b) Use the number line to add (−5) and (+7).
Start at (−5) and move 7 in the positive direction.

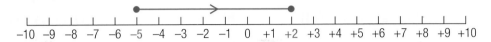

So

$$(-5) + (+7) = (+2) \quad \text{or } 2$$

c) Use a number line to calculate (+6) − (+2).
Start at (+6) and move 2 in the negative direction.

So

$$(+6) - (+2) = (+4) \quad \text{or } 4$$

d) Use a number line to calculate (−2) − (+3).
Start at (−2) and move 3 in the negative direction.

So

$$(-2) - (+3) = (-5) \quad \text{or } -5$$

e) Use a number line to calculate (−3) − (−6).
Start at (−3) and move 6 in the positive direction.

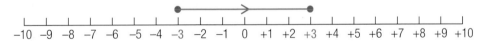

So

$$(-3) - (-6) = (+3) \quad \text{or } 3$$

EXERCISE 8.1A

Work out the answers to the following calculations. You may need to use a number line.

1 **a)** (+5) + (−3) **b)** (+7) + (−4) **c)** (+10) + (−6)

2 **a)** (−3) + (+5) **b)** (−7) + (+5) **c)** (−8) + (−7)

3 **a)** (−5) + (−4) **b)** (−7) + (−1) **c)** (−7) + (−5)   →

4 a) (−5) + (+4) + (−1) **b)** (−8) + (−5) + (+6) **c)** (+7) + (−6) + (−3)

5 a) (+9) − (+4) **b)** (+5) − (+3) **c)** (+11) − (+4)

6 a) (+13) − (+4) **b)** (+4) − (+6) **c)** (+12) − (+5)

7 a) (−6) − (+3) **b)** (−4) − (+14) **c)** (−22) − (+12)

8 a) (−9) − (−15) **b)** (−3) − (−12) **c)** (−4) − (−11)

Multiplying and dividing integers

(+3) × (+2) means   3 lots of +2   or   (+2) + (+2) + (+2) = (+6)
(+3) × (−2) means   3 lots of −2   or   (−2) + (−2) + (−2) = (−6)
(−3) × (+2) means   −3 lots of +2   or   −((+2) + (+2) + (+2)) = −(6) = (−6)
(−3) × (−2) means   −3 lots of −2   or   −((−2) + (−2) + (−2)) = −(−6) = (+6)

When multiplying:
- a positive number by a positive number, the result is positive
- a positive number by a negative number, the result is negative
- a negative number by a positive number, the result is negative
- a negative number by a negative number, the result is positive.

EXERCISE 8.1B

1 Work out the following.
   a) (+8) × (−6)   **b)** (+6) × (−5)   **c)** (+4) × (−7)

2 Work out the following.
   a) (−5) × (+4)   **b)** (−7) × (+9)   **c)** (−7) × (+7)

3 Copy and complete this multiplication grid.

×	−3	−2	−1	0	+1	+2	+3
+3			−3			+6	
+2							
+1					+2		
0		0			0		
−1						−3	
−2							
−3							

4 Work out the following.
    a) $(+4) \times (+2)$ **b)** $(-3) \times (+1)$ **c)** $(+3) \times (-4)$
    d) $(-2) \times (-5)$ **e)** $(-5) \times (-1)$ **f)** $(-3) \times (-3)$

The rules for **division** of integers are the same as those above for multiplication. When both quantities are positive or both are negative, the result is positive. When one is positive and the other is negative, the result is negative.

Worked examples

a) $(+12) \div (-3) = -4$

b) $(-12) \div (-3) = +4$

EXERCISE 8.1C

1 Calculate the following.
    a) $(+18) \div (+6)$ **b)** $(+18) \div (-6)$ **c)** $(-18) \div (+6)$
    d) $(-18) \div (-6)$ **e)** $(-24) \div (-6)$ **f)** $(-25) \div (+5)$

2 Copy and complete the following, writing in the missing numbers to make the calculations correct.
    a) _____ $\times (+5) = (+25)$ **b)** _____ $\times (-3) = (-21)$
    c) _____ $\times (-5) = (-20)$ **d)** $(-7) \times$ _____ $= (-28)$
    e) $(+6) \times$ _____ $= (-42)$ **f)** $(-8) \times$ _____ $= (+32)$

3 The table gives pairs of numbers x and y which add together to make 8. That is,
$$x + y = 8.$$

Copy and complete the table.

x	+5	+4	+3	+2	+1	0	−1	−2	−3	−4	−5
y											

4 If $p + q = -3$, copy and complete this table.

p	+5	+4	+3	+2	+1	0	−1	−2	−3	−4	−5
q											

5 If $xy = +24$, copy and complete this table.

x	+4	+3	+2	+1	−1	−2	−3	−4
y								

xy means x multiplied by y.

Factors, prime numbers and prime factors

Factors of a number are all the whole numbers (positive integers) which divide exactly into that number. For example, the factors of 18 are all the numbers which divide into 18 exactly. They are 1, 2, 3, 6, 9 and 18.

A **prime number** is a number which has only two factors, 1 and itself.

By definition, 1 is not a prime number.

A **prime factor** is a factor of a number which is also a prime number. Therefore, the prime factors of 15 are 3 and 5. We can find the prime factors of a number by constructing a factor tree.

Worked examples

a) Find the prime factors of 45.

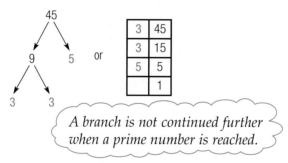

A branch is not continued further when a prime number is reached.

So the prime factors of 45 are 3 and 5.

b) Express 45 as a product of primes.
From the factor tree above we can see that 45 can be written as **3 × 3 × 5** or, using indices, as $3^2 \times 5$. *3^2 means 3×3.*

EXERCISE 8.2A

1 List all the factors of the following numbers and circle the prime factors.
   a) 66   **b)** 75   **c)** 28   **d)** 48   **e)** 120

2 Find the prime factors of the following numbers. Express each number as a product of prime numbers, using indices when needed.
   a) 12   **b)** 64   **c)** 72   **d)** 80   **e)** 144

Highest common factor and lowest common multiple

The factors of 20 are 1, 2, 5, 10 and 20.
   The factors of 30 are 1, 2, 3, 5, 6, 10, 15 and 30.
   The largest factor to appear in both groups is 10, so 10 is the **highest common factor** (HCF) of 20 and 30.

The multiples of 6 are those numbers in the 6× table, i.e. 6, 12, 18, 24, 30, etc.
The multiples of 8 are those numbers in the 8× table, i.e. 8, 16, 24, 32, 40, etc.
The smallest multiple to appear in both groups is 24, so 24 is the **lowest common multiple** (LCM) of 6 and 8.

EXERCISE 8.2B

1 Find the highest common factor of the following numbers.
   a) 9, 12   **b)** 15, 25   **c)** 12, 18, 36
   d) 14, 21, 35   **e)** 36, 63, 108

2 Find the lowest common multiple of the following numbers.
   a) 6, 16   **b)** 4, 10   **c)** 2, 5, 10
   d) 3, 7, 10   **e)** 3, 7, 15

Powers and roots

Squares

The numbers 1, 4, 9, 16 are **square numbers**, and are made by multiplying an integer (whole number) by itself. For example,

$$8 \times 8 = 64$$

therefore 64 is a square number.

But

$$2.3 \times 2.3 = 5.29$$

5.29 is *not* a square number as 2.3 is not an integer.

Squaring a number is multiplying a number by itself. For example,
   8 squared is 8×8
   2.3 squared is 2.3×2.3

There is a short way to write a number squared. It involves using **indices**.
For example,

$$8 \times 8 = 8^2$$
$$2.3 \times 2.3 = 2.3^2$$

Using a calculator

The 'squared' button on the calculator usually looks like this: $\boxed{x^2}$

Worked example

Use a calculator to evaluate 17^2.

$$\boxed{1}\ \boxed{7}\ \boxed{x^2}\ \boxed{=}\ \boxed{\text{289}}$$

Square roots

The **inverse** (opposite) operation to addition is subtraction, and the inverse operation to multiplication is division. Squaring also has an inverse operation.

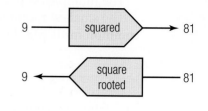

From what you learned about the multiplication of integers earlier in this chapter, you know that $-9 \times -9 = 81$.

So $(-9)^2$ is $+81$. Therefore -9 is also a square root of 81.

Every positive integer has a positive and a negative square root.

Using a calculator

All scientific calculators can work out the **square root** of a number by using the $\boxed{\sqrt{}}$ key.

Worked example

Use a calculator to work out $\sqrt{729}$.

$$\boxed{\sqrt{}}\ \boxed{7}\ \boxed{2}\ \boxed{9}\ \boxed{=}\ \boxed{27}$$

These instructions are for calculators that use direct algebraic logic. For some calculators, particularly older ones, the calculation needs to be entered differently. Check how yours works.

Calculations without a calculator

Worked examples

a) Without using a calculator evaluate $\sqrt{0.36}$.
    0.36 can be written as a fraction.

$$0.36 = \frac{36}{100}$$

$$\sqrt{0.36} = \frac{\sqrt{36}}{\sqrt{100}} = \frac{6}{10}$$

$$\frac{6}{10} = 0.6$$

Therefore $\sqrt{0.36} = 0.6$ and -0.6

b) Without using a calculator evaluate $\sqrt{0.81}$.
    0.81 can be written as a fraction.

$$0.81 = \frac{81}{100}$$

$$\sqrt{0.81} = \frac{\sqrt{81}}{\sqrt{100}} = \frac{9}{10}$$

$$\frac{9}{10} = 0.9$$

Therefore $\sqrt{0.81} = 0.9$ and -0.9

EXERCISE 8.3A

1 Without using a calculator, calculate how many squares of side length 1 cm there are in squares with the following side lengths.
   a) 13 cm   **b)** 15 cm   **c)** 18 cm
   d) 11 cm   **e)** 12 cm   **f)** 100 cm

2 Without using a calculator, work out the square roots of the following numbers.
Give positive and negative roots.
   a) 25   **b)** 49   **c)** 121
   d) 169   **e)** 0.04   **f)** 0.25

3 Use the $\boxed{\sqrt{}}$ key on your calculator to check your answers to question 2.

4 Evaluate the following without using a calculator.
Give positive and negative roots.
   a) $\sqrt{\dfrac{1}{9}}$ **b)** $\sqrt{\dfrac{1}{25}}$ **c)** $\sqrt{\dfrac{4}{25}}$

   d) $\sqrt{\dfrac{49}{100}}$ **e)** $\sqrt{\dfrac{25}{144}}$ **f)** $\sqrt{\dfrac{49}{121}}$

5 Without using a calculator, work out the positive and negative square roots of the following decimals.
   a) 0.25   **b)** 0.49   **c)** 0.64
   d) 0.81   **e)** 1.44   **f)** 1.69

Cubes

This pattern sequence is made up of 1 cm cubes.

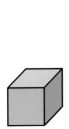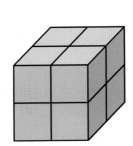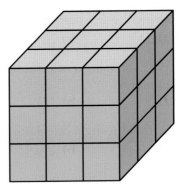

The 1 cm × 1 cm × 1 cm cube contains *one* 1 cm × 1 cm × 1 cm cube.
The 2 cm × 2 cm × 2 cm cube contains *eight* 1 cm × 1 cm × 1 cm cubes.
The 3 cm × 3 cm × 3 cm cube contains *27* 1 cm × 1 cm × 1 cm cubes.

The numbers 1, 8, and 27 are **cube numbers**, and are made by multiplying an integer by itself three times. For example,

$$5 \times 5 \times 5 = 125$$

Therefore 125 is a cube number.

Cubing a number is multiplying a number by itself three times. As with squaring, there is a short way to write a number cubed using indices. For example,

$$5 \times 5 \times 5 = 5^3$$

Using a calculator

Not many calculators have a specific $\boxed{x^3}$ key. However, all scientific calculators have an 'indices' key. The indices key looks like this: $\boxed{y^x}$. It allows a number to be raised to any power, not just cubed.

Worked example

Use a calculator to work out 8^3.

$$\boxed{8}\ \boxed{y^x}\ \boxed{3}\ \boxed{=}\ \boxed{512}$$

Cube roots

The inverse of cubing a number is finding its **cube root**, written as $\sqrt[3]{\ }$. So $\sqrt[3]{125}$ is 5 and $\sqrt[3]{343}$ is 7 (since $7 \times 7 \times 7 = 343$).

EXERCISE 8.3B

1 How many $1\,\text{cm} \times 1\,\text{cm} \times 1\,\text{cm}$ cubes would make up cubes with the following side lengths?
   a) 4 cm   **b)** 6 cm   **c)** 10 cm   **d)** 9 cm

2 Using the $\boxed{y^x}$ button on your calculator, evaluate the following.
   a) 11^3 **b)** 20^3 **c)** 2.5^3 **d)** 6.2^3

3 Without using a calculator, work out the cube roots of the following numbers.
   a) 8   **b)** 125   **c)** 27   **d)** 1000

4 Without using a calculator if possible, work out the following.
   a) $\sqrt[3]{64}$ **b)** $\sqrt[3]{343}$ **c)** $\sqrt[3]{216}$ **d)** $\sqrt[3]{8000}$

5 Check your answers to questions 3 and 4 using a calculator.

Index notation for positive integer powers

8×8 can be written as 8^2.
    We read this as '8 squared'.

Similarly, $7 \times 7 \times 7$ can be written as 7^3.
    We read it as '7 cubed'.

Also, $6 \times 6 \times 6 \times 6$ can be written as 6^4.
    We read it as '6 to the power of 4'.

EXERCISE 8.3C

1 Write each of these using index notation.
   a) $9 \times 9 \times 9$ **b)** $6 \times 6 \times 6 \times 6 \times 6$
   c) $5 \times 5 \times 5 \times 5$ **d)** $8 \times 8 \times 8 \times 8 \times 8 \times 8$
   e) $2 \times 2 \times 2 \times 2 \times 2 \times 2 \times 2 \times 2 \times 2$

2 Write each of these numbers in full and find its value.
   a) 3^4 **b)** 2^5 **c)** 5^4 **d)** 10^6 **e)** 4^3

9 Equations and simple functions

◆ Know that algebraic operations, including brackets, follow the same order as arithmetic operations; use index notation for small positive integer powers.

◆ Construct and solve linear equations with integer coefficients (unknown on either or both sides, without or with brackets).

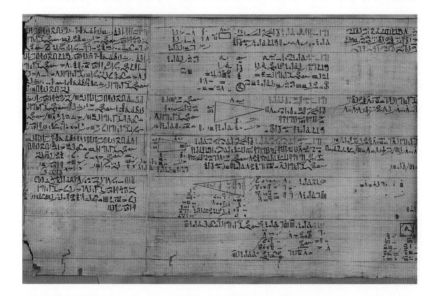

The Rhind mathematical papyrus is the best remaining example of Egyptian mathematics. It dates from around 1650 BCE and is 33 cm tall and over 5 metres long. It is named after Alexander Rhind, who bought it in Luxor, Egypt in 1858.

> *Papyrus is a type of paper.*

The papyrus was copied by Ahmose, a scribe, who describes it as giving 'accurate reckoning for inquiring into things, and the knowledge of all things, mysteries ... all secrets'. It began to be mathematically translated in the late 19th century. In 2011, the mathematical translation is still incomplete.

The first part of the Rhind papyrus consists of reference tables and a collection of 40 algebraic problems of different sorts, from simple fractional expressions to linear equations. This papyrus covers other areas of mathematics as well.

Order of operations and algebra

Calculations need to be carried out in a particular order. As you already know, this order is not necessarily from left to right.

For example, the calculation $2 + 5 \times 8$ has the answer 42 (rather than 56) because the multiplication is done before the addition.

The order in which operations are carried out is as follows:

> Brackets
> Indices
> Division and/or Multiplication
> Addition and/or Subtraction

A useful way of remembering the order is with the shorthand **BIDMAS**.
The same order of operations applies when working with algebraic expressions.

Worked examples

a) Simplify the expression $3a + 4a \times 5 - 2a$. *The multiplication is done first.*

$3a + 4a \times 5 - 2a$

$= 3a + 20a - 2a$ *Additions and subtractions can be done in any order.*

$= 21a$

b) Simplify the expression $3p + 5(4p - 6) - 7p$.

$3p + 5(4p - 6) - 7p$ *The brackets are expanded first.*

$= 3p + 20p - 30 - 7p$

$= 16p - 30$

EXERCISE 9.1

Simplify the following expressions using the correct order of operations.

1 $3a + 5(2a + 6) - 7a$

2 $6b - 8(4b - 9) + 3b$

3 $3(4c - 10) + 2(c - 1)$

4 $9(8d - 3) - 8(5d + 4)$

5 $-4(4e - 7) - 9(7e + 6) + 10$

6 $20 - 2(4f - 9) + 7(2f - 6) + 11$

7 $-4(7 + 6g) - 7(-8g + 1)$

8 $3 + 4(7 - h) - 4(3h - 1)$

9 $4i + 7i - (i - 9) + 2$

10 $3(4j + 2) - 5(2j - 6) + 4(6j - 1)$

Indices

The expressions a^2, b^3 and y^5 are examples of numbers raised to a **power**. We say 'a to the power of 2' (or 'a squared'), 'b to the power of 3' (or 'b cubed') and 'y to the power of 5'.

The small number is called an **index**. The plural of index is **indices**.

Expressions like this can be added, subtracted, multiplied and divided. You will learn more about indices in Student's Book 3 but for now you only need to know that

$$a^2 + a^2 = 2a^2$$

This can be explained by looking at a square tile of side length a like this:

a

a

Its area is $a \times a = a^2$.

If two of these tiles are placed side by side, the total area of the rectangle is

$$2a \times a = 2a^2$$

a

a a

The area of the rectangle must be the same as the sum of the areas of the two squares separately, which is $a^2 + a^2$. Therefore

$$a^2 + a^2 = 2a^2$$

Similarly,

$$7b^2 - 3b^2 = 4b^2$$

In the expression $5a^2 + 2a^2 + 4a + 9a$, you can add $5a^2$ and $2a^2$, and $4a$ and $9a$, to give

$$5a^2 + 2a^2 + 4a + 9a = 7a^2 + 13a$$

But you cannot add $7a^2$ and $13a$ together as they are not **like terms**.

Worked examples

a) Simplify the expression $5(4c - 1) + 6(c^2 - 4)$.

$5(4c - 1) + 6(c^2 - 4)$

$= 20c - 5 + 6c^2 - 24$ (expand the brackets)

$= 6c^2 + 20c - 29$ (simplify by adding like terms)

b) Simplify the expression $5(2j + 3) - 5(2j^2 - 6) + 5(6j^3 - 1)$.

$5(2j + 3) - 5(2j^2 - 6) + 5(6j^3 - 1)$

$= 10j + 15 - 10j^2 + 30 + 30j^3 - 5$ (expand the brackets)

$= 30j^3 - 10j^2 + 10j + 40$ (simplify by collecting like terms)

Simplify the following expressions using the correct order of operations.

1 $3a^2 + 5(2a + 4) - 3a$

2 $6b - 8(4b^2 - 1) + 3b$

3 $3(4c - 10) + 2(c^2 - 1)$

4 $2(8d - 3) - 2(5d^2 + 4)$

5 $-3(2e - 7) + 5(7e + 6)$

6 $-2(4f^2 - 1) + 7(2f^2 - 3)$

7 $-4(7 + 6g) - 7(-8g^2 + 1)$

8 $4(7 - h^3) + 4(h^3 - 1)$

9 $4i + 7i - (i - 9) + 2i^4$

10 $2(4j + 2) + 3(2j^2 - 6) + 4(6j - 1)$

Further equations

An equation represents two quantities that are equal to each other. In Student's Book 1 we saw that, to help understand what an equation is and how it can be manipulated, it can be thought of as a pair of balanced scales.

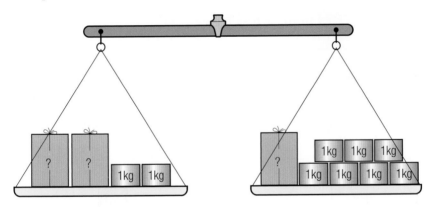

In the scales above there are two different types of object: 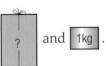 and 1kg .

The left-hand side of the scales balances the right-hand side, i.e. the total masses on both sides are equal.

Worked example

For the scales on page 87, find the mass of each 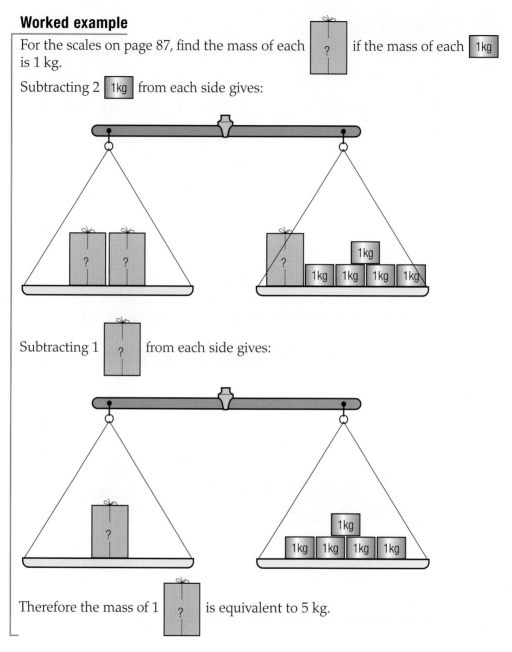 if the mass of each 1kg is 1 kg.

Subtracting 2 1kg from each side gives:

Subtracting 1 ? from each side gives:

Therefore the mass of 1 ? is equivalent to 5 kg.

However, drawing scales at each stage in the solution can be a time-consuming process. A quicker way is to use algebra instead of diagrams. The problem above can be written as:

$$2x + 2 = x + 7 \quad \text{where } x \text{ is the mass of 1 } \boxed{?}.$$

To solve the equation:
$$2x + 2 = x + 7$$
$$2x = x + 5 \qquad \text{(subtract 2 from each side)}$$
$$x = 5 \qquad \text{(subtract } x \text{ from each side)}$$

More complicated equations can be solved in the same way as long as the fundamental rule of equation solving is used, i.e. what is done to one side of the equation must also be done to the other.

Worked examples

a) Solve the equation $4x - 6 = 2x + 2$.
$$4x - 6 = 2x + 2$$
$$2x - 6 = 2 \qquad \text{(subtract } 2x \text{ from both sides)}$$
$$2x = 8 \qquad \text{(add 6 to both sides)}$$
$$x = 4 \qquad \text{(divide both sides by 2)}$$

b) Solve the equation $15 = 24 + 3x$.
$$15 = 24 + 3x$$
$$-9 = 3x \qquad \text{(subtract 24 from both sides)}$$
$$-3 = x \qquad \text{(divide both sides by 3)}$$

c) Solve the equation $4(m + 3) = 32 + 2m$.
$$4(m + 3) = 32 + 2m$$
$$4m + 12 = 32 + 2m \qquad \text{(expand the brackets)}$$
$$2m + 12 = 32 \qquad \text{(subtract } 2m \text{ from both sides)}$$
$$2m = 20 \qquad \text{(subtract 12 from both sides)}$$
$$m = 10 \qquad \text{(divide both sides by 2)}$$

d) Solve the equation $3(x - 7) = 2(2x - 15)$.
$$3(x - 7) = 2(2x - 15)$$
$$3x - 21 = 4x - 30 \qquad \text{(expand the brackets)}$$
$$-21 = x - 30 \qquad \text{(subtract } 3x \text{ from both sides)}$$
$$9 = x \qquad \text{(add 30 to both sides)}$$

EXERCISE 9.3A

Solve these equations.

1 **a)** $a + 4 = 6$ **b)** $2a + 5 = 11$ **c)** $3a + 9 = 21$
   d) $4a + 5 = 29$ **e)** $5a + 3 = 28$

2 **a)** $b - 3 = 4$ **b)** $2b - 6 = 8$ **c)** $3b - 9 = 12$
   d) $4b - 1 = 19$ **e)** $5b - 8 = 32$

3 **a)** $4c = 3c + 4$ **b)** $6c = 5c + 8$ **c)** $8c = 7c + 3$
   d) $5c = 4 + 4c$ **e)** $7c = 8 + 6c$

4 **a)** $3d = 2d - 2$ **b)** $5d = 4d - 4$ **c)** $6d = 5d - 9$
   d) $8d = 7d - 11$ **e)** $10d = 9d - 9$

5 **a)** $3e = e + 4$ **b)** $6e = 3e + 12$ **c)** $5e = e + 8$
   d) $7e = 2e + 20$ **e)** $11e = 4e + 21$

6 **a)** $4f = 2f - 6$ **b)** $5f = 2f - 9$ **c)** $8f = 4f - 24$
   d) $9f = 4f - 20$ **e)** $12f = 7f - 35$

7 **a)** $5 = g + 9$ **b)** $9 = g - 3$ **c)** $8 = 2g + 2$
   d) $14 = 3g + 2$ **e)** $28 = 6g - 8$

8 **a)** $2(h + 1) = 6$ **b)** $3(h + 2) = 18$ **c)** $4(h + 5) = 40$
   d) $7(h - 3) = 14$ **e)** $9(h - 7) = 36$

9 **a)** $4 + 3k = 4k - 2$ **b)** $5k + 7 = 3k + 15$ **c)** $6k - 3 = 3k + 12$
   d) $2k + 16 = 10k - 16$ **e)** $8 - 3k = 2k - 2$

10 **a)** $2(l - 3) = 4(l - 6)$ **b)** $2(l + 1) = 3(l - 5)$ **c)** $5(l - 4) = 3(l + 2)$
   d) $6(2l + 3) = 5(4l + 2)$ **e)** $7(7 + 2l) = 3(9l - 1)$

EXERCISE 9.3B

Solve these equations.

1 **a)** $2(3 - f) = 4$ **b)** $6(7 - f) = 12$ **c)** $5(9 - f) = 20$
   d) $11(16 - f) = 22$ **e)** $3(8 - f) = 21$

2 **a)** $2(h + 2) = 8$ **b)** $3(h + 1) = 12$ **c)** $4(h + 5) = 60$
   d) $8(h + 3) = 48$ **e)** $9(h + 5) = 72$

3 **a)** $\dfrac{j}{4} = 2$ **b)** $\dfrac{j}{5} = 3$ **c)** $\dfrac{j}{8} = 4$

   d) $\dfrac{j}{7} = 2$ **e)** $\dfrac{j}{9} = 3$

4 **a)** $\dfrac{2k}{3} = 4$ **b)** $\dfrac{3k}{2} = 6$ **c)** $\dfrac{5k}{3} = 10$

   d) $\dfrac{8k}{5} = 24$ **e)** $\dfrac{7k}{8} = 14$

Constructing and solving equations

Sometimes you will be asked to use some information you are given to construct (make) an equation and then use algebra to solve the equation.

Worked example

Ayse and Ahmet are playing a 'think of a number' game.
Ayse says, 'I think of a number, double it and subtract 5. The answer is 27.'
What is the number Ayse chose?

Using n to represent the number Ayse chose, we can write:
$$2n - 5 = 27$$

Then we solve the equation as before:
$$2n = 27 + 5$$
$$2n = 32$$
$$n = 16$$

So the number she chose is 16.

Construct an equation from the information given in each question and then solve it.

1 I think of a number and add 10. The answer is 24. What is the number?

2 I think of a number and subtract 7. The answer is 7. What is the number?

3 A number times 7 is 42. What is the number?

4 A number divided by 11 is 3. What is the number?

5 I think of a number and add 17. The answer is 54. What is the number?

6 I think of a number and subtract 33. The answer is 5. What is the number?

7 A number times 11 is 132. What is the number?

8 A number divided by 13 is 4. What is the number?

9 I think of a number and add 8. The answer is 32. What is the number?

10 I think of a number and subtract 37. The answer is 27. What is the number?

Constructions

◆ Know that the longest side of a right-angled triangle is called the hypotenuse.

◆ Use a straight edge and compasses to construct:
   – the midpoint and perpendicular bisector of a line segment
   – the bisector of an angle.

◆ Use a ruler and compasses to construct:
   – circles and arcs
   – a triangle, given three sides (SSS)
   – a triangle, given a right angle, hypotenuse and one side (RHS).

Constructing circles and circle patterns

A variety of different shapes can be constructed using a ruler and a pair of compasses. Doing this accurately requires practice and care.

Check that the compass screw is tightened, to prevent the compasses from widening as the circle is drawn, and use a sharp pencil.

EXERCISE 10.1

1 Draw the following circles using a pair of compasses. In each case *O* is the centre.

a)
5 cm

b)
6 cm

c)
3.5 cm

d)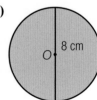
8 cm

2 Draw the following circle patterns using a pair of compasses.

a)   b)   c)

d)

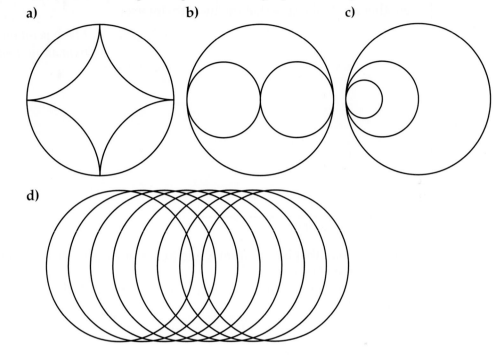

3 Draw three circle patterns of your own.

Constructing triangles

A triangle can be constructed in various ways depending on the information given. If some angles are given, then a ruler and protractor are used, as you saw in Student's Book 1. If, however, only the lengths of the three sides of the triangle are given (SSS), then a pair of compasses are necessary for the construction.

Worked example

Construct the triangle XYZ, where the length $XY = 10$ cm, $XZ = 8$ cm and $YZ = 6$ cm. Use a ruler and a pair of compasses only.

- First use a ruler to draw a line 10 cm long and label its ends X and Y.
- Open your compasses to 8 cm. Place the compass point on X and draw an **arc**.

Every point on the arc is 8 cm away from X.

X ─────────────── Y
           10cm

- Open your compasses to 6 cm. Place the compass point on Y and draw another arc. Make sure that the two arcs intersect.

> *Every point on the arc is 6 cm away from Y.*

The only point that is 8 cm from X and 6 cm from Y is where the two arcs intersect. Label this point Z.
- Finally, draw straight lines from X to Z and from Y to Z. This completes the triangle XYZ.

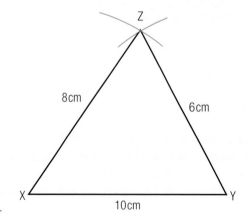

EXERCISE 10.2A

For questions 1–4, construct the triangles PQR using only a ruler and a pair of compasses. For each triangle, measure accurately each of the angles P, Q and R.

1 $PQ = 6$ cm $PR = 8$ cm $QR = 10$ cm

2 $PQ = 12$ cm $PR = 9$ cm $QR = 5$ cm

3 $PQ = 4$ cm $PR = 7$ cm $QR = 7$ cm

4 $PQ = 6.2$ cm $PR = 6.2$ cm $QR = 6.2$ cm

5 Name the type of triangle constructed in each of questions 1–4.

Right-angled triangles

In a right-angled triangle, two of the sides are **perpendicular** (at right angles) to each other. The third side (the one that is opposite the right angle) is the longest side and is called the **hypotenuse**.

A right-angled triangle can be constructed using a ruler and a pair of compasses.

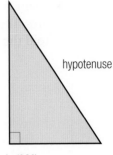

hypotenuse

right angle (90°)

Worked example

Construct the right-angled triangle *ABC*, where the length *AB* = 6 cm and the hypotenuse *BC* = 11 cm.

- Using a ruler, draw a line longer than 6 cm. Mark off a 6 cm length and label it *AB*.

- Open the pair of compasses to about 2 cm. Place the compass point on *A* and mark two arcs on the line, one either side of point *A*.

- Open the compasses further, to about 4 cm. Place the compass point on the intersection of the line and one of the small arcs and draw another arc above *A*.

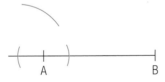

- Keeping the same radius, place the point on the intersection of the line with the other small arc and draw another arc above *A*. Make sure that it intersects the first one.

- Using a ruler, draw a line from point *A* through the intersection of the two arcs. This line is perpendicular to *AB*, so the point *C* will be on it. As we are not told the length of *AC*, extend the line beyond the intersection of the two arcs.

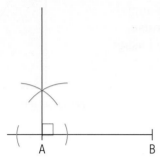

- The hypotenuse is the side opposite the right angle. Open the compasses to 11 cm. Place the compass point on *B* and draw an arc so that it intersects the line which is perpendicular to *AB*.

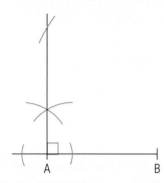

- Label the point of intersection *C*. Use a ruler to draw the line *BC*. This completes the triangle *ABC*.

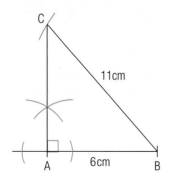

EXERCISE 10.2B

Construct the following right-angled triangles using only a ruler and a pair of compasses. For each triangle, measure accurately the length of the third side.

1
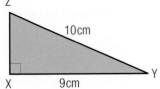

2
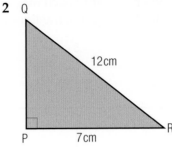

3
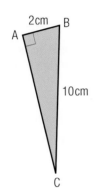

4
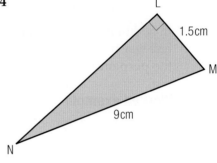

5 In the triangle *DEF*, the length *DX* = 4 cm, *XE* = 6 cm and *EF* = 8 cm.
   a) Using a pair of compasses and a ruler only, construct the triangle *DEF*.
   b) Measure the length of the side *DF*.
   c) Measure the height of the triangle, *XF*.

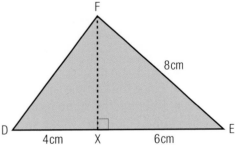

6 In the obtuse-angled triangle *PQR*, *PX* and *XR* are perpendicular to each other.
   The length *XQ* = 5 cm, *PQ* = 10 cm and *PR* = 15 cm.
   a) Construct the triangle *PQR* using only a ruler and a pair of compasses.
   b) Measure the length of *QR*.
   c) Measure the size of the angle *PQR*.

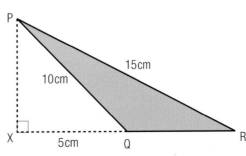

Perpendicular bisector and the midpoint

Lines that are at right angles to each other are said to be **perpendicular**. The right-angled triangles in the previous section had two sides which were perpendicular to each other.

In this diagram, the lines *PQ* and *ST* are perpendicular to each other.

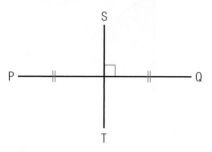

In addition, *ST* passes through the **midpoint** of *PQ*, that is, the point which is half way between *P* and *Q*. Therefore *ST* **bisects** *PQ* (it divides it in half). *ST* is the **perpendicular bisector** of *PQ*.

Worked example

Construct the perpendicular bisector of a line using a ruler and a pair of compasses.

- Draw a line and label it *AB*.

- Open a pair of compasses to more than half the distance *AB*.
- Place the compass point on *A* and draw arcs above and below *AB*.
- Keeping the same radius, place the compass point on *B* and draw arcs above and below *AB*. Make sure that they intersect the first pair of arcs.

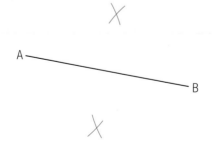

● Draw a line through the two points where the arcs intersect.

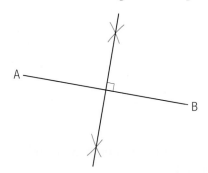

This line is the perpendicular bisector of AB, as it divides AB in half and also meets it at right angles.

EXERCISE 10.3

1 Copy each of the lines drawn below (actual size) on to plain paper and construct the perpendicular bisectors.

a) ⎯⎯⎯⎯⎯⎯⎯⎯
7 cm

b)
11 cm

c)
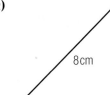
8 cm

d)
9 cm

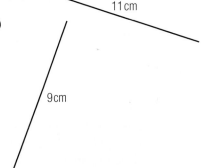

2 Copy this diagram.

●A

●B

●C

a) Construct the perpendicular bisector of *AB*.
b) Construct the perpendicular bisector of *BC*.
c) What can be said about the point of intersection of the two perpendicular bisectors?
d) Construct the perpendicular bisector of *AC*. What do you notice?
e) Is it possible to draw a circle so that points *A*, *B* and *C* all lie on the circumference of the circle? Explain your answer.

3 Draw a triangle *XYZ* with three acute angles.

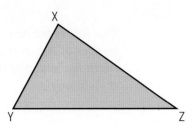

By construction, draw a circle to pass through points *X*, *Y* and *Z*. This is called the **circumcircle** of the triangle.

4 Draw a triangle *PQR* with an obtuse angle at *P*.

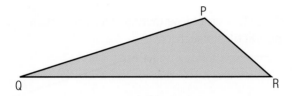

By construction, draw a circle to pass through points *P*, *Q* and *R*.

Bisecting an angle

Just as bisecting a line means dividing it into two halves, bisecting an angle means splitting the angle in half too.

Bisecting an angle properly does not involve using a protractor. Instead, a pair of compasses should be used.

Worked example

Bisect the angle *A* using a pair of compasses.

- Open the pair of compasses. Place the compass point on *A* and draw two small arcs so that they intersect each of the arms of the angle.

- Place the compass point on each of the points where the arcs intersect the lines and draw two more arcs that intersect. Make sure the radius remains unchanged.

- With a ruler, draw a straight line from A through the point of intersection of these two arcs. This line is the angle bisector of A.

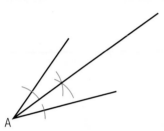

EXERCISE 10.4

For questions 1–4, draw angles similar to the ones shown. Bisect each of them using only a ruler and a pair of compasses.

1

2

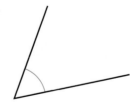

3

4

5   **a)** Using only a ruler and a pair of compasses, construct two lines which are perpendicular to each other.

    b) Bisect the right angle. What size angle has been constructed?

6 **a)** Construct an equilateral triangle *ABC* of side length 6 cm.
   b) (i) Bisect angle *A*.
   (ii) Extend the bisecting line until it intersects the side *BC*. Label this point *X*.
   (iii) Describe the triangle *ABX*.

For questions 7–11, use only a ruler and a pair of compasses to construct the following shapes.

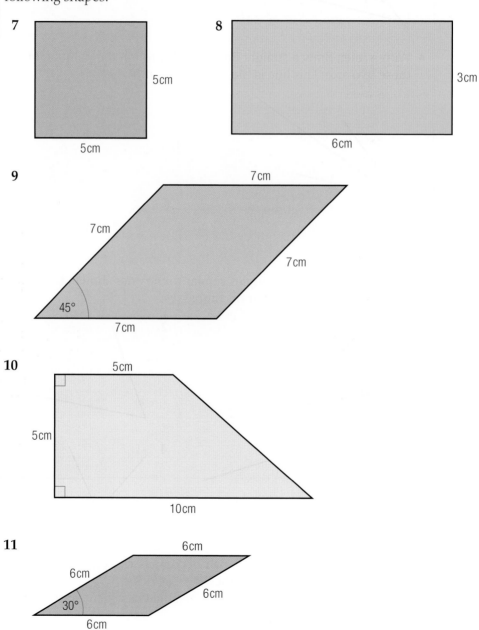

11 Transformations

◆ Find the midpoint of the line segment *AB*, given the coordinates of points *A* and *B*.

◆ Transform two-dimensional shapes by rotation, reflection and translation, and simple combinations of these transformations.

The midpoint of a line segment

A **line segment** is part of a line and has a fixed length. This is in contrast to a **line**, which is of infinite length.

The **midpoint** of a line segment is the point exactly half way along its length.

If the coordinates of the two end points of a line segment are known, it is possible to calculate the coordinates of its midpoint and also the length of the line segment (dealt with in Student's Book 3).

Worked example

Two points $A = (3, 1)$ and $B = (9, 5)$ are joined by the straight-line segment *AB*. Calculate the coordinates of the midpoint *M* of *AB*.

The diagram shows points *A* and *B* and the line segment joining them, plotted on a coordinate grid.

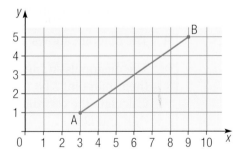

The horizontal distance between *A* and *B* is $9 - 3 = 6$ units.

The vertical distance between *A* and *B* is $5 - 1 = 4$ units.

The midpoint is at the point which is half of each of these distances away from *A* and *B*. That is, it is $6 \div 2 = 3$ units horizontally from *A* (and *B*) and $4 \div 2 = 2$ units vertically from *A* (and *B*).

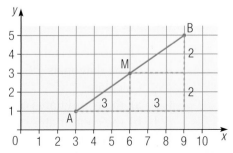

Therefore the coordinates of the midpoint *M* are $(3 + 3, 1 + 2) = (6, 3)$.

The calculation can be simplified as follows. The x and y coordinates of the midpoint of a line segment are the means of the x and y coordinates of the end points of the line segment. In the example on page 103, the coordinates of M are

$$\left(\frac{3+9}{2}, \frac{1+5}{2}\right) = (6,3)$$

In general:

If the coordinates of the two end points of a line segment are (x_1, y_1) and (x_2, y_2), the coordinates of the midpoint are $\left(\dfrac{x_1 + x_2}{2}, \dfrac{y_1 + y_2}{2}\right)$.

EXERCISE 11.1

1 For each of the following pairs of points:
   (i) plot the points on a coordinate grid and join them with a line segment
   (ii) calculate the coordinates of the midpoint of the line segment.

   a) $A = (1, 3)$ and $B = (7, 5)$
   b) $X = (2, 1)$ and $Y = (4, 7)$
   c) $P = (-5, 1)$ and $Q = (6, 1)$
   d) $L = (-6, 4)$ and $M = (-6, 9)$
   e) $J = (-2, -3)$ and $K = (-5, 2)$
   f) $C = (-1, 8)$ and $D = (2, -3)$

2 A line segment AB has midpoint $M = (3, 5)$ and the coordinates of point A are $(7, 3)$. Calculate the coordinates of point B.

3 A line segment ST has midpoint $M = (-2, 4)$ and the coordinates of point T are $(1, 9)$. Calculate the coordinates of point S.

4 The diagram shows a square $ABCD$.

The diagonals AC and BD intersect at their midpoint $M = (0, -2)$.
Calculate the coordinates of the vertices A, B and D.

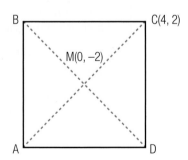

5 The diagram shows a parallelogram $DEFG$.

The point M is the midpoint of the diagonals DF and EG.
Calculate:
   a) the coordinates of M
   b) the coordinates of the vertex D.

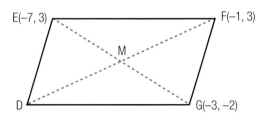

Transformations

In Student's Book 1 you studied some of the basic transformations.
These included reflections, rotations and translations. For example,

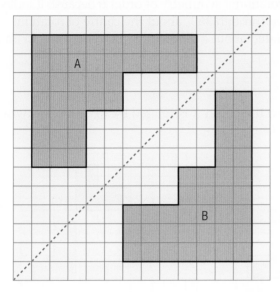

Object *A* is **reflected** in the mirror line to map on to image *B*.

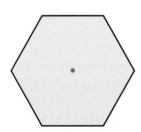

This object has **rotational** symmetry of order 6.

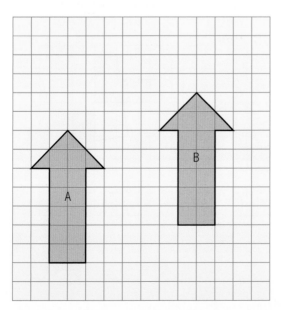

Object *A* maps on to image *B* by a **translation** of 7 units to the right and 2 units upwards.

Rotation about a point

You already know that some shapes have **rotational symmetry** because they look exactly the same more than once when rotated about a point. The regular hexagon on page 105 has rotational symmetry of order 6 because it looks the same *six* times when rotated through 360° about the centre of rotation.

An object can also be rotated about a different point to produce an image in a different place.

Worked examples

a) Draw the image *Y* when the object *X* is rotated by 90° anti-clockwise about the centre of rotation *O*.

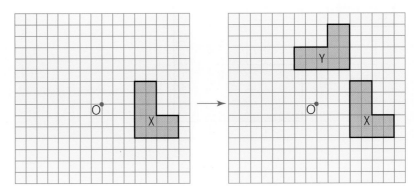

> *With a rotation, the object and image are congruent, i.e. exactly the same size and shape.*

Every point on *X* is rotated by 90° anti-clockwise about *O* to the corresponding point on the image *Y*. The diagram below shows this for two of the points.

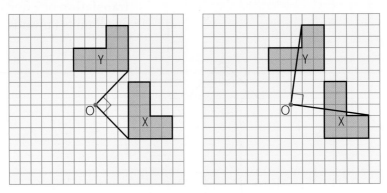

b) Draw the image R when the object P is rotated by 180° about the centre of rotation O.

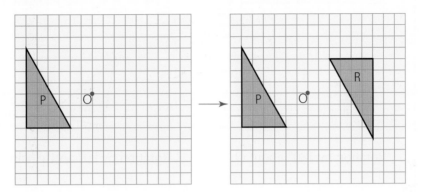

Once again, each point on the object is rotated by 180° about the centre of rotation, as shown below.

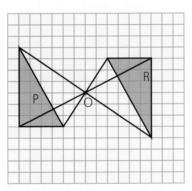

EXERCISE 11.2A

In each of the following questions, copy the grid and the object A. Draw the image B when the object is rotated by the angle stated, about the centre of rotation O.

1

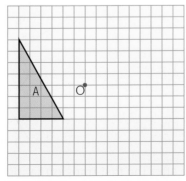

Rotation by 90° clockwise about O

2

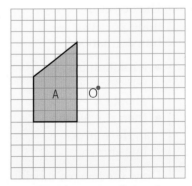

Rotation by 180° about O

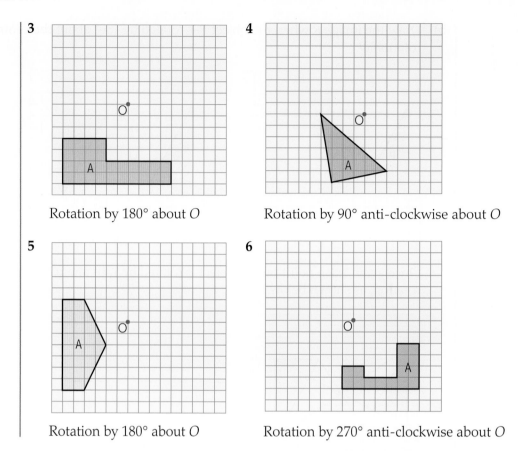

3 Rotation by 180° about O

4 Rotation by 90° anti-clockwise about O

5 Rotation by 180° about O

6 Rotation by 270° anti-clockwise about O

Combining transformations

All of the transformations you have met so far have been carried out as a single transformation. However, it is possible to *combine* transformations, so that an object undergoes more than one transformation to map it on to an image.

The types of transformations and the order in which they are carried out affect where the image appears.

Worked example

The object *A* undergoes two transformations:

- a rotation by 90° clockwise about *O*
- then a reflection in the mirror line shown.

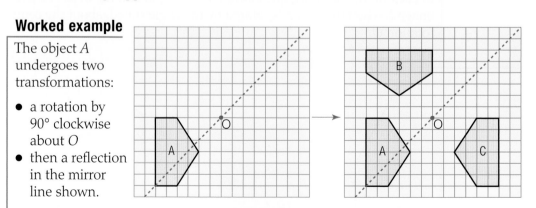

Draw the images, labelling the image after the first transformation *B* and the image after the second transformation *C*.

EXERCISE 11.2B

In each of the following questions, the object X undergoes two transformations. The first transformation maps X on to an image Y, the second maps Y on to an image Z.

Copy each diagram on to squared paper and draw each of the images Y and Z, labelling them clearly.

1

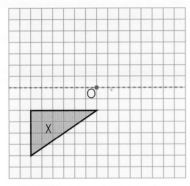

Reflection in the mirror line
Rotation by 90° clockwise about O

2

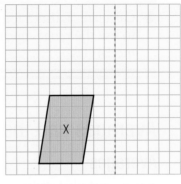

Translation by 2 units to the right
and 7 units upwards
Reflection in the mirror line

3

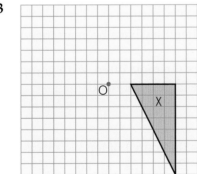

Translation by 6 units upwards
Rotation by 180° about O

4

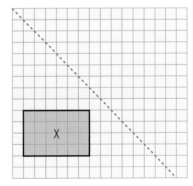

Reflection in the mirror line
Translation by 1 unit to the right
and 8 units downwards

12 Statistical calculations

◆ Calculate statistics for sets of discrete and continuous data; recognise when to use the range, mean, median and mode and, for grouped data, the modal class.

Averages and the range

Averages

You are already familiar with the most common types of statistical calculations that can be carried out on a set of data. These are the different types of average: the mean, the median and the mode.

- The **mean** is $\dfrac{\text{the sum of all the values}}{\text{the number of values}}$.
- The **median** is the middle value when they have been arranged in order of size.
- The **mode** is the value which occurs the most often. With grouped data, the **modal group** is the group with the largest frequency.

Worked example

The data below represents the masses (in grams) of ten biscuits in a packet.

| 24 | 23 | 21 | 24 | 24 | 22 | 26 | 24 | 21 | 22 |

Calculate the mean, median and modal mass of the biscuits in the packet.

$$\text{Mean} = \frac{24 + 23 + 21 + 24 + 24 + 22 + 26 + 24 + 21 + 22}{10} = \frac{231}{10} = 23.1\,\text{g}$$

To calculate the median, first arrange the data in order of size:

| 21 | 21 | 22 | 22 | 23 | 24 | 24 | 24 | 24 | 26 |

As the number of values is even, there is not a middle value but a middle *pair* (circled).

The median is the mean of the middle pair, i.e. $\dfrac{23 + 24}{2} = 23.5\,\text{g}$.

The mode is 24 as that is the value which occurs the most often. Therefore the modal mass is 24 g.

If the data is presented in a frequency table, the mean, median and mode can still be calculated.

Worked example

This frequency table shows the numbers of sweets in 15 packets of the same brand.
    Calculate the mean, median and modal numbers of sweets in a packet.
    There are 2 packets with 20 sweets, 4 packets with 21 sweets, 8 packets with 22 sweets and 1 packet with 23 sweets. So the total number of sweets in the 15 packets is:

Number of sweets	Frequency
20	2
21	4
22	8
23	1

$$(20 \times 2) + (21 \times 4) + (22 \times 8) + (23 \times 1) = 323$$

So the mean number of sweets in a packet is:

$$\text{mean} = \frac{323}{15} = 21.53.$$

The median *can* be calculated by re-writing all the data values in order and choosing the middle value:

$$20 \quad 20 \quad 21 \quad 21 \quad 21 \quad 21 \quad \text{etc.}$$

However, this method is not very efficient, as the frequency table already shows the data in order. There are 15 data values so the middle value is the eighth value, as there will be seven values below it and seven above it. Counting from either end of the table, we can see that the eighth value is 22. Therefore the median number of sweets is 22.
    The modal number of sweets is the value with the highest frequency. Therefore the modal number of sweets is 22.

The range

Another useful calculation that can be carried out on a set of data is to find the **range**. The range is the difference between the greatest value and the smallest value. It gives a measure of how *spread out* the data is.

    Using the masses of the biscuits from the example on page 110, the highest mass was 26 g and the lowest mass was 21 g. Therefore:

$$\text{range} = 26\,\text{g} - 21\,\text{g} = 5\,\text{g}$$

The range can also be calculated from a frequency table. Using the numbers of sweets in a packet from the example above, we can see from the table that the smallest number of sweets in a packet was 20 and the greatest was 23. Therefore:

$$\text{range} = 23 - 20 = 3$$

Worked examples

A group of boys and a group of girls in the same class took the same test. The frequency tables below show their marks out of 10.

Marks out of 10 (boys)	Frequency		Marks out of 10 (girls)	Frequency
1	1		1	0
2	0		2	0
3	0		3	0
4	2		4	2
5	2		5	4
6	3		6	6
7	4		7	1
8	2		8	1
9	0		9	0
10	1		10	0

a) Calculate the range of marks for the boys and for the girls.
b) Comment on any differences.

a) Highest mark for the boys = 10
Lowest mark for the boys = 1
Range for the boys = 10 – 1 = 9
Highest mark for the girls = 8
Lowest mark for the girls = 4
Range for the girls = 8 – 4 = 4
b) The range of the boys' marks is greater than the girls'. This indicates that the boys' marks are more spread out or *less consistent*.

EXERCISE 12.1

1 A man travels to work by bus each morning. Sometimes the bus is late. Over a 20-day period he keeps a record of how many minutes late the bus is each day. The results are given below.

0 0 1 0 3 2 0 0 10 3 2 1 0 0 2 2 25 1 22 0

Calculate:
a) the mean number of minutes that the bus is late
b) the median number of minutes that the bus is late
c) the modal number of minutes that the bus is late
d) the range of minutes that the bus is late.

2 The weights (in kilograms) of ten puppies from the same litter are recorded below.

   1.23   1.42   2.01   1.56   1.66   0.92   1.38   1.44   1.52   1.48

Calculate:

a) the mean weight
b) the median weight
c) the modal weight
d) the range of their weights.

3 15 students in a class are each asked how many brothers and sisters they have.
The results are shown below.

Number of brothers and sisters	0	1	2	3	4	5	6
Frequency	3	6	3	2	0	0	1

a) Calculate the mean, median and modal numbers of brothers and sisters.
b) Calculate the range of the data.

4 As part of a traffic survey, the woman conducting the survey stands by the side of a road. She counts the number of people in each car as it passes her. The frequency table shows the results.

Number of people	Frequency
1	22
2	10
3	5
4	1
5	1
6	2
7	6

a) How many cars were included in the survey?
b) How many people travelling by car were counted in the survey?
c) Calculate the mean number of people in each car.
d) Calculate the median number of people in each car.
e) (i) What is the greatest number of people counted in a car?
   (ii) What is the smallest number of people counted in a car?
   (iii) Calculate the range of the numbers of people travelling in a car. ➡

5 A tomato grower trials a new type of plant food to see if the number of tomatoes per plant increases as a result. 20 tomato plants are given just water and another 20 are given the new plant food. He counts and records the number of tomatoes, of a certain size, that each plant produces. The two sets of data are given in the tables.

Plants given water only

Number of tomatoes per plant	30	31	32	33	34	35	36	37	38	39	40
Frequency	2	3	3	4	4	2	1	0	0	0	1

Plants given new food

Number of tomatoes per plant	30	31	32	33	34	35	36	37	38	39	40
Frequency	3	3	1	1	0	0	0	4	4	1	3

a) Calculate the mean, median and mode of the number of tomatoes produced per plant for each set of data.

b) Calculate the range for each set of data.

c) Comment on any differences that you found in parts a) and b) and decide whether the new food affects the number of tomatoes produced per plant.

Reliability of statistical calculations

Statistical calculations are carried out to summarise data. However, it is often said that statistics can be used to mislead. It is important to know as much as possible about the data and the methods of calculation before accepting any conclusions that are made.

The following table highlights the strengths and weaknesses of the different types of statistical calculation you have met so far.

Calculation	Strengths	Weaknesses
Mean	Takes all of the data into account Is the type of average understood by most people	Can be distorted by extreme results May not be a possible value for the data
Median	Takes all of the data into account Not affected by extreme values Easy to calculate	May not be a possible value for the data
Mode	Not affected by extreme values Easy to calculate Will always be a possible value for the data	The data may not have a mode or there may be several modes For grouped data, only a modal group can be given Does not take all of the data into account
Range	Easy to calculate Good for comparisons between data sets	Does not take all the data into account Can be distorted by extreme results

Worked examples

The lifetimes (hours of continuous use in the same test) of ten batteries are shown below.

2	2	1	3	3	2	2	1	1	83

The manufacturer claims that 'on average' their batteries last 10 hours.
a) Is the claim true?
b) Is the claim misleading?
c) What value for the average would you choose, and why?

a) Calculating each of the three averages gives:
   mean = 10 hours
   median = 2 hours
   mode = 2 hours

   Strictly speaking, the claim is true. The manufacturer is taking the mean value as the average.

b) The claim is misleading because the mean calculation has been affected by the one extreme result. Neither the median nor the mode has been affected by this result.

c) Assuming that the intention is not to mislead, then either the median or the modal lifetime would be better.

EXERCISE 12.2

1 Two groups of ten students take the same maths test. One group is from a class which is set by ability, and the other is from a mixed ability class. The table shows their results.

Group A results	0	1	2	3	5	5	7	8	9	10
Group B results	5	5	5	5	5	5	5	5	5	5

   a) Calculate the mean, median and modal results for each group.
   b) Explain why none of the averages is useful for deciding which group is from which class.
   c) Explain why calculating the range is helpful in this case.

2 A small company has seven employees and one manager. Their annual salaries are shown below.
   $6000 $8000 $7500 $10 000
   $8000 $120 000 $7000 $8000

   The company wishes to employ another person. The job advertisement states that the average salary in the company is approximately $21 800.
   a) Calculate the mean, median and modal salaries.
   b) Comment on whether the claim in the advertisement is true.
   c) Comment on whether you think the claim is misleading.

→

3 Two train companies publish data about how punctual their trains are. The data, which shows how many minutes late the trains are, is given in the table.

	Mean	Median	Mode	Range
Company A	10	3	1	54
Company B	8	8	8	4

a) Which train company is more consistent? Explain your answer.

b) Give a possible reason why the mean result for company A is so much higher than its median or mode.

c) Both companies want to advertise how punctual their trains are. Write a short sentence that each company might use for an advertising campaign.

d) Which company's trains do you think perform better? Justify your answer.

4 The table shows the midday temperatures (in °C) at two ski resorts over a 14-day period.

Midday temperature in resort X (°C)	−8	−6	−5	−5	−4	−3	−2	−1	0	1	1	4	4	4
Midday temperature in resort Y (°C)	−4	−3	−1	−1	−1	−1	−1	−1	0	0	0	0	1	1

a) Calculate the mean, median, mode and range for both resorts.

b) Resort X wishes to suggest that its temperatures are colder than those of resort Y. Write a sentence it could use to say this.

c) Resort Y wishes to suggest that its temperatures are colder than those of resort X. Write a sentence it could use to say this.

5 'The average number of legs per human is less than two.' Comment on this statement.

13 Calculations and mental strategies 2

◆ Use known facts to derive new facts, e.g. given $20 \times 38 = 760$, work out 21×38.
◆ Consolidate adding and subtracting integers and decimals, including numbers with differing numbers of decimal places.

Mental strategies

You should already know basic multiplication facts up to 10×10. You can use these facts, or facts that you are given, to work out more complicated multiplications in your head.

Worked examples

a) Multiply **(i)** 50×7 **(ii)** 51×7

  (i) We know that $5 \times 7 = 35$.
     50 is ten times bigger than 5,
     so 50×7 must be ten times bigger than 5×7.
     $50 \times 7 = 35 \times 10 = 350$

  (ii) We have found that $50 \times 7 = 350$.
     $51 \times 7 = (50 \times 7) + (1 \times 7) = 350 + 7 = 357$

b) Multiply **(i)** 70×80 **(ii)** 72×80

  (i) We know that $7 \times 8 = 56$.
     70 is ten times bigger than 7 and 80 is ten times bigger than 8,
     so 70×80 must be *one hundred* times bigger than 7×8.
     $70 \times 80 = 56 \times 100 = 5600$

  (ii) We have found that $70 \times 80 = 5600$.
     $72 \times 80 = (70 \times 80) + (2 \times 80) = 5600 + 160 = 5760$

c) Multiply **(i)** 600×40 **(ii)** 600×43

  (i) We know that $6 \times 4 = 24$.
     600 is one hundred times bigger than 6 and 40 is ten times bigger than 4,
     so 600×40 must be *one thousand* times bigger than 6×4.
     $600 \times 40 = 24 \times 1000 = 24\,000$

  (ii) We have found that $600 \times 40 = 24\,000$.
     $600 \times 43 = (600 \times 40) + (600 \times 3) = 24\,000 + 1800 = 25\,800$

EXERCISE 13.1

Multiply the following pairs of numbers in your head, without looking at a multiplication grid or using a calculator. Write down your answers.

1 a) 20×5 **b)** 23×5 **c)** 23×50 **d)** 23×51

2 a) 60×3 **b)** 61×3 **c)** 61×30 **d)** 61×31

3 a) 40×5 **b)** 42×5 **c)** 42×50 **d)** 42×51

4 a) 9×30 **b)** 90×30 **c)** 92×30 **d)** 92×31

5 a) 20×5 **b)** 22×5 **c)** 22×50 **d)** 220×5.1

6 a) 60×9 **b)** 61×9 **c)** 61×0.9 **d)** 61×0.91

7 a) 6×8 **b)** 60×80 **c)** 60×83 **d)** 61×83

8 a) 9×30 **b)** 9×33 **c)** 9×3.3 **d)** 0.9×0.33

9 a) 2×38 **b)** 2×3.8 **c)** 20×3.8 **d)** 21×3.8

10 a) 4×32 **b)** 4×3.2 **c)** 0.4×3.2 **d)** 0.4×0.32

Written methods

There are different written methods for adding and subtracting. The examples below show one method for each. If you prefer a different method and it works, then continue to use it.

Worked examples

a) Add the following numbers.

6.035   29   0.071   147.30

First write the four numbers so that the decimal points line up.

```
      6 . 0 3 5
    2 9 . 0 0 0
      0 . 0 7 1
+ 1 4 7 . 3 0 0
  1 8 2 . 4 0 6
    2       1
```

If the total of any column is 10 or more, the tens are carried over to the next column (as shown in red).

b) Subtract 75.97 from 200.03.

```
  1  9  9    9
  2  Ø  Ø . Ø  1  3
-    7  5 . 9  7
  1  2  4 . 0  6
```

If the digit on top is smaller than the digit below, a ten is carried over from the next column.

The answer can be checked by addition:

```
    1 2 4 . 0 6
  +   7 5 . 9 7
  ─────────────
    2 0 0 . 0 3
    1 1 1   1
```

EXERCISE 13.2A

Without using a calculator, work out these additions.

1	3.32 + 8.7	**2**	12.09 + 4.6
3	15.875 + 3.08	**4**	643 + 9.67
5	13.08 + 62.6	**6**	543.67 + 14.9
7	3 + 17.09	**8**	9.045 + 8.006
9	77 + 45.4	**10**	12.6 + 8.5

EXERCISE 13.2B

Without using a calculator, work out these calculations.

1	14.23 − 6.87	**2**	18 − 11.68
3	19 − 13.09	**4**	14.3 − 8.23
5	20 − 14.098	**6**	17 − 9.6 + 2.45
7	12 − 8.098 + 1.23	**8**	14.6 − 6.78 + 12.409
9	18.456 − 11 + 0.76	**10**	19 − 93.6 + 106.45

EXERCISE 13.2C

1 Work out these calculations.
   a) $7.43 + $8.29
   b) $300 − $237.57
   c) $88.62 + $30.82 + $405.60
   d) $100 − $56.30 − $23.88

2 A glass of water with capacity 275 m*l* is filled from a bottle containing 2.5 litres of water. How much water is left in the bottle after:
   a) one glass of water is poured?
   b) three glasses of water are poured?
   c) nine glasses of water are poured?

→

3 A family of five people check in their suitcases at the airport. The weights of the five cases are 15.5 kg, 20.2 kg, 16 kg, 17.4 kg and 13.7 kg.
   a) Calculate the total weight of the cases.
   b) The weight limit for the five cases is 85 kg.
      Calculate how much extra weight the family could have carried.

4 A girl is 97 cm tall. She needs to be at least 1.3 m tall before she can go on a particular ride at a theme park. How much more does the girl need to grow before she will be allowed on the ride?

5 A bridge over a road is 4.2 m high at its lowest point. A truck 3.65 m high passes under the bridge. Calculate the height of the gap between the bridge and the truck, giving your answer in centimetres.

6 A pizzeria offers the following pizzas for sale.
   A group of friends order two Margherita pizzas, one La Reine pizza, two Veneziana pizzas and one Fiorentina pizza.

Margherita	$5.25
La Reine	$6.15
Veneziana	$6.85
Fiorentina	$7.25

   a) Calculate the total cost of the pizzas.
   b) They pay for the pizzas with $40.
      Calculate the amount of change they are due.
   c) Is the change enough for a 10% tip?
      If it is not enough, how much more is needed?

7 A plane is flying at 7560.6 metres above the sea. It drops a sonar beacon to the ocean floor. The beacon falls 8655.37 metres. How deep is the ocean at this point?

8 Find the new temperature for each of the following. You may need to draw a number line.
   a) The temperature was −1.18 °C and rises by 12.6 °C.
   b) The temperature was −18.66 °C and rises by 20.7 °C.
   c) The temperature was −2.9 °C and rises by 6.25 °C.
   d) The temperature was −0.35 °C and falls by 8.17 °C.

9 A woman's bank account shows a balance of $1360.50 in credit.
   Work out her final balance as a positive or negative number after each of these amounts has been paid or received:
   a) Pay car payment $250.45
   b) Pay rent $1650
   c) Receive salary $2102.78
   d) Pay credit card $564.77
   e) Pay electricity bill $432.07
   f) Pay for holiday $760

10 A mine shaft is 6250 m deep. There is one tunnel 3400 m down from the top of the shaft and another tunnel 600 m up from the bottom. What is the distance between the tunnels?

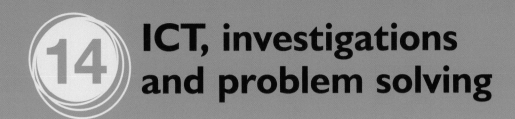

14 ICT, investigations and problem solving

1 Four, three, two, one

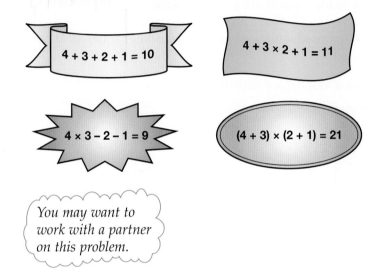

4 + 3 + 2 + 1 = 10

4 + 3 × 2 + 1 = 11

4 × 3 − 2 − 1 = 9

(4 + 3) × (2 + 1) = 21

You may want to work with a partner on this problem.

All these calculations contain the numbers 4, 3, 2 and 1, in that order. Addition, subtraction, multiplication and brackets have been used to make the results 9, 10, 11 and 21.

a) How many different results can you make using only addition, subtraction, multiplication and brackets?

b) Now reverse the order to 1, 2, 3, 4 (or your partner could do this). Can you make more results than before, or fewer?

c) Does one of the arrangements produce more results than the other?

⭐ **d)** Can other results be produced if the four numbers can be arranged in *any* order?

2 Chessboards

A normal chessboard is an 8 × 8 square made from 64 unit squares like this:

Smaller 'chessboards' can also be made using unit squares in a similar way.

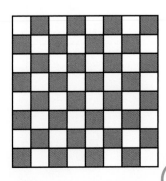

a) For example, here is a 3 × 3 chessboard:

> **(i)** How many squares are touching *two* other squares in the 3 × 3 chessboard? Where are they situated?
> **(ii)** How many squares are touching *three* other squares? Where are they situated?
> **(iii)** How many squares are touching *four* other squares? Where are they situated?

Assume that a square 'touches' another square only if their sides are next to each other.

b) Now think about a 4 × 4 chessboard:

> **(i)** How many squares are touching *two* other squares? Where are they situated?
> **(ii)** How many squares are touching *three* other squares? Where are they situated?
> **(iii)** How many squares are touching *four* other squares? Where are they situated?

c) Repeat the questions above for a 5 × 5 chessboard.

d) Enter your results into a spreadsheet similar to the one shown below.

Side length	Chessboard dimensions	Number of squares touching		
		2 squares	3 squares	4 squares
2	2 × 2	4	0	0
3	3 × 3			
4	4 × 4			
5	5 × 5			

e) If possible, use a formula in the spreadsheet to generate the results for chessboards up 8 × 8.

Side length	Chessboard dimensions	Number of squares touching		
		2 squares	3 squares	4 squares
2	2 × 2	4	0	0
3	3 × 3			
4	4 × 4			
5	5 × 5			
6	6 × 6			
7	7 × 7			
8	8 × 8			

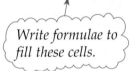

Write formulae to fill these cells.

f) (i) How many squares are touching *two* other squares on an $m \times m$ chessboard?

(ii) How many squares are touching *three* other squares on an $m \times m$ chessboard?

(iii) How many squares are touching *four* other squares on an $m \times m$ chessboard?

Review 2A

1 Work out the following.
   a) $(+7) + (+5) - (+6) - (+3)$
   b) $(-4) - (-6) + (-9) - (+7)$
   c) $(-5) \times (+4) \times (-3) \times (+6)$
   d) $(+18) \div (+6) \times (-3) \times (+2)$

2 Find the prime factors of the following numbers. Express each number as a product of prime numbers, using indices when needed.
   a) 2310
   b) 1440

3 Evaluate the following without using a calculator.
   Give positive and negative roots.

   a) $\sqrt{\dfrac{4}{9}}$

   b) $\sqrt{\dfrac{81}{25}}$

   c) $\sqrt{\dfrac{144}{289}}$

4 Simplify the following expressions using the correct order of operations.
   a) $11a^2 + 3(4a + 2) - 13a$
   b) $9b - (7b^2 - 11) + b$
   c) $6(7c - 2) + 4(c^2 - 8)$

5 Solve the following equations.
   a) $2x - 5 = 3(x + 1)$
   b) $\dfrac{2x - 2}{3} = 4$
   ⭐ **c)** $3x + 1 = 2$

6 I have ten full boxes of counters and one box with 12 counters missing. There are 153 counters altogether. How many counters are in each full box?

7 **a)** Using a protractor, draw an angle of 50°.
   b) Using a pair of compasses, bisect your angle. Leave any construction lines visible.

8 This diagram shows a triangle labelled *A*.
Copy the diagram on to squared paper and on
the same grid draw the images of the triangle
after the following transformations in turn:
   a) a rotation by 180° about *O*
      (label this image *B*)
   b) then a reflection in the mirror line
      (label this image *C*).

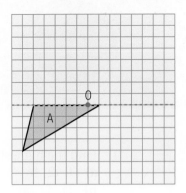

9 25 students in a class are asked how many cars their family has.
The table shows the results.

Number of cars	0	1	2	3	4
Frequency	6	9	7	2	1

   a) Calculate the mean, median and modal number of cars per family.
   b) Calculate the range of the data.

10 Find the new temperature for each of the following. You may need to draw a
number line.
   a) The temperature was −13.58 °C and rises by 19.1 °C.
   b) The temperature was −1.66 °C and falls by 7.7 °C.
   c) The temperature was 2.9 °C and falls by 9.89 °C.

1 Find the highest common factor of the following numbers.
   a) 4, 12, 16
   b) 21, 42, 56
   c) 36, 54, 108

2 Find the lowest common multiple of the following numbers.
   a) 3, 8, 16
   b) 4, 7, 10
   c) 3, 5, 7

3 Without using a calculator, work out the positive and negative square roots of the following decimals.
   a) 0.81
   b) 1.21
   c) 2.25

4 Without using a calculator if possible, work out the following.
   a) $\sqrt[3]{125}$
   b) $\sqrt[3]{512}$
   c) $\sqrt[3]{1331}$

5 Simplify the following expressions using the correct order of operations.
   a) $6i + i - 3(2i - 9) + 8i^4$
   b) $6(j + 2) + 5(j^2 - 2) - 7(2j - 4)$

★ 6 A number has 7 subtracted from it and the result is multiplied by 6. The answer is the same as doubling the number, subtracting 15 and then multiplying by 4.
   a) Construct an equation from the information given.
   b) Solve the equation to find the number.

7 Draw a triangle ABC similar to this.

   Using a pair of compasses:
   a) construct the perpendicular bisector of AC
   b) construct the perpendicular bisector of BC.
   c) Use your constructions in parts a) and b) to construct a circle that passes through A, B and C.

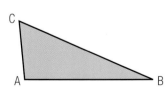

8 Copy the shape below on to squared paper and draw the image after a rotation by 270° clockwise about the centre of rotation *O*.

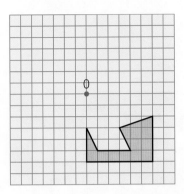

9 Two bus companies publish data about how punctual their buses are. The data, which shows how many minutes late the buses are, is given in the table.

	Mean	Median	Mode	Range
Company A	10	10	1	28
Company B	10	10	10	0

    a) Which bus company is more consistent? Explain your answer.

    b) Both companies want to promote their service. Write a short sentence that each company might use for an advertising campaign.

    c) Which company's buses do you think perform better? Justify your answer.

10 A plane is flying 9350 metres above the *bottom* of the sea. It drops a float to the surface of the sea. A submarine is directly below the plane.

    a) The float falls 7542 metres. How deep is the sea at that point?

    b) The submarine is 670 metres below the surface. How far is the plane above it?

SECTION 3

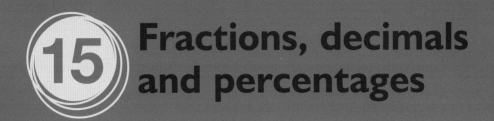

Fractions, decimals and percentages

15

◆ Convert a fraction to a decimal using division; know that a recurring decimal is a fraction.
◆ Order fractions by writing with common denominators or dividing and converting to decimals.
◆ Add and subtract fractions and mixed numbers; calculate fractions of quantities (fraction answers); multiply and divide an integer by a fraction.
◆ Find equivalent fractions, decimals and percentages by converting between them.
◆ Calculate and solve problems involving percentages of quantities and percentage increases or decreases; express one given number as a fraction or percentage of another.

Fractions and decimals

Fractions

Fractions deal with a part of a whole. A fraction has two parts: the **numerator** and the **denominator**.

The numerator is the number above the line, whilst the denominator is the number below the line, i.e.

$$\frac{\text{numerator}}{\text{denominator}}$$

Both the numerator and denominator must be **integers** (whole numbers).

Decimals

Decimals are another way of writing parts of a whole number. For example, the fraction $\frac{1}{8}$ can be written as a decimal as 0.125. To convert a fraction to a decimal, simply divide the numerator by the denominator.

Worked example

Write $\frac{3}{8}$ as a decimal.

$$3 \div 8 = 0.375$$

This can be done using a calculator or by division.

Therefore $\frac{3}{8}$ as a decimal is 0.375.

EXERCISE 15.1A

Convert the following fractions to decimals by dividing the numerator by the denominator.

1 a) $\frac{3}{5}$ b) $\frac{4}{5}$ c) $1\frac{2}{5}$

2 a) $\frac{1}{4}$ b) $\frac{3}{4}$ c) $2\frac{3}{4}$

3 a) $\frac{3}{8}$ b) $\frac{5}{8}$ c) $\frac{7}{8}$

4 a) $\frac{11}{20}$ b) $\frac{17}{20}$ c) $\frac{19}{20}$

5 a) $\frac{16}{25}$ b) $\frac{19}{25}$ c) $\frac{24}{25}$

6 a) $\frac{1}{40}$ b) $\frac{17}{40}$ c) $\frac{17}{80}$

There are different types of decimal. One of those types is called a **terminating** decimal.

A terminating decimal comes to an end, for example 0.625.

Worked example

Convert $\frac{1}{5}$ to a decimal.

$$\frac{1}{5} = 0.2$$

0.2 is a terminating decimal.

All the decimals calculated in Exercise 15.1A were terminating decimals.

Changing a decimal to a fraction

All terminating decimals can be written as fractions. In order to do this, an understanding of place value is necessary.

Worked examples

a) Write the decimal 0.7 as a fraction in its simplest form.

By entering 0.7 into a place value table we get:

Units	•	Tenths
0	•	7

The 7 is worth 7 tenths. As a fraction, this can therefore be written as $\frac{7}{10}$.

b) Write the decimal 0.625 as a fraction in its simplest form.

By entering 0.625 into a place value table we get:

Units	•	Tenths	Hundredths	Thousandths
0	•	6	2	5

6 tenths, 2 hundredths and 5 thousandths is equivalent to 625 thousandths.

As a fraction, this can therefore be written as $\frac{625}{1000}$.

$\frac{625}{1000}$ can be simplified to $\frac{5}{8}$.

EXERCISE 15.1B

Convert each of the following decimals to a fraction in its simplest form.

1 **a)** 0.6   **b)** 0.9   **c)** 0.3

2 **a)** 0.25   **b)** 0.75   **c)** 1.25

3 **a)** 0.45   **b)** 0.65   **c)** 2.85

4 **a)** 0.125   **b)** 0.875   **c)** 0.375

Ordering fractions

Unless fractions are written with the same denominator, it can be difficult to see which fraction is bigger and which is smaller. For example, with the fractions $\frac{5}{12}$ and $\frac{7}{12}$, it is easy to see that $\frac{7}{12}$ is the larger of the two fractions. However, with $\frac{4}{9}$ and $\frac{5}{12}$ it is not quite so straightforward.

In order to compare and order fractions, it is usual to write them as **equivalent fractions** with the same denominator. Another way is to change them to decimals first.

Worked example

Write the following fractions in order, smallest first.

$$\frac{3}{7} \qquad \frac{8}{21} \qquad \frac{1}{3}$$

Looking at the denominators, we can identify 21 as being the **lowest common multiple** of 7, 21 and 3. Writing each of the fractions as an equivalent fraction with a denominator of 21 gives:

$$\frac{3}{7} = \frac{9}{21} \qquad \frac{8}{21} \qquad \frac{1}{3} = \frac{7}{21}$$

Therefore the fractions in ascending order are: $\frac{1}{3}, \frac{8}{21}, \frac{3}{7}$.

Alternatively, changing the fractions to decimals gives:

$$\frac{3}{7} = 0.428... \qquad \frac{8}{21} = 0.380... \qquad \frac{1}{3} = 0.333...$$

It is easy to see that the order is: 0.333..., 0.380..., 0.428..., i.e. $\frac{1}{3}, \frac{8}{21}, \frac{3}{7}$.

EXERCISE 15.1C

Answer these questions either by changing the fractions to equivalent fractions with the same denominator or by changing them to decimals.

1 Write down whether each of the following statements is true or false.

    a) $\frac{2}{4}$ is greater than $\frac{3}{8}$ **b)** $\frac{2}{5}$ is less than $\frac{6}{10}$

    c) $\frac{4}{12}$ is equal to $\frac{1}{3}$ **d)** $\frac{19}{20}$ is greater than $\frac{8}{10}$

    e) $\frac{8}{15}$ is less than $\frac{3}{5}$ **f)** $\frac{5}{8}$ is equal to $\frac{54}{88}$

2 Write each of the following sets of fractions in order, smallest first.

    a) $\frac{5}{9}, \frac{2}{3}, \frac{3}{6}$ **b)** $\frac{3}{7}, \frac{5}{14}, \frac{9}{28}$ **c)** $\frac{6}{13}, \frac{25}{52}, \frac{10}{26}$ **d)** $\frac{14}{15}, \frac{27}{30}, \frac{59}{60}$

3 In a tennis match player A managed to get $\frac{13}{25}$ of her first serves in. Player B managed to get $\frac{2}{5}$ of her first serves in. Which player got a higher proportion of her first serves in?

4 Two schools hold their school play on the same evening. At one school, $\frac{7}{20}$ of the audience are children. At the other, $\frac{2}{5}$ of the audience are children. Which school has the highest proportion of children in the audience?

5 A tropical fruit juice states on the label that it is made up of the following fractions of fruit:

    $\frac{1}{4}$ orange $\frac{1}{8}$ mango $\frac{3}{16}$ passion fruit $\frac{7}{32}$ pineapple $\frac{15}{64}$ grape

    Write down the fruits in ascending order of their proportion in the juice.

Calculating with fractions

Calculating fractions of a quantity

To work out a fraction of an amount, look at the fraction itself for help. The denominator tells us how many equal parts the amount is split into, whilst the numerator indicates how many of the parts are being used. Any quantity left over (a remainder) is a fraction.

Worked examples

a) Evaluate $\frac{7}{8}$ of 35.

$\frac{1}{8}$ of 35 is worked out like this:

$$35 \div 8 = 4 \text{ with } 3 \div 8 \text{ left over.}$$

This can be written as a mixed number as $4\frac{3}{8}$.

$\frac{7}{8}$ of 35 is seven times as much as $\frac{1}{8}$.

Therefore $\frac{7}{8}$ of 35 is

$$(7 \times 4) + \left(7 \times \frac{3}{8}\right) = 28 + \frac{21}{8}$$
$$= 28 + 2\frac{5}{8}$$
$$= 30\frac{5}{8}$$

b) A teenager spends $\frac{3}{5}$ of his money on clothes. If he has \$32, calculate how much he spends on clothes.

$\frac{1}{5}$ of \$32 is worked out like this:

$$\$32 \div 5 = \$6 \text{ remainder } 2, \text{ or } \$6\frac{2}{5}, \text{ i.e. } \$6.40.$$

$\frac{3}{5}$ of \$32 is three times as much as $\frac{1}{5}$.

Therefore $\frac{3}{5}$ of \$32 is $3 \times \$6.40 = \$19.20$.

So the teenager spends \$19.20 on clothes.

c) A park has 57 flower beds. There are enough plants for $\frac{5}{8}$ of the flower beds to be planted. Calculate:
(i) the exact number of flower beds planted
(ii) the number of flower beds left unplanted.

(i) $\frac{1}{8}$ of 57 is $57 \div 8 = 7$ remainder 1, or $7\frac{1}{8}$.

$\frac{5}{8}$ of 57 is five times as much as $\frac{1}{8}$.

Therefore $\frac{5}{8}$ of 57 is $5 \times 7\frac{1}{8} = 35\frac{5}{8}$.

There are enough plants to plant $35\frac{5}{8}$ flower beds.

(ii) There are $57 - 35\frac{5}{8} = 21\frac{3}{8}$ flower beds left unplanted.

EXERCISE 15.2A

For questions 1–5, give your answers as mixed numbers.

1 Work out the following.
    a) $\frac{1}{5}$ of 46   **b)** $\frac{2}{5}$ of 46   **c)** $\frac{3}{5}$ of 46

2 Work out the following.
    a) $\frac{1}{8}$ of 65   **b)** $\frac{3}{8}$ of 65   **c)** $\frac{7}{8}$ of 65

3 Work out the following.
    a) $\frac{1}{10}$ of 133   **b)** $\frac{5}{10}$ of 133   **c)** $\frac{9}{10}$ of 133

4 Work out the following.
    a) $\frac{1}{8}$ of 169   **b)** $\frac{5}{8}$ of 169   **c)** $\frac{7}{8}$ of 169

5 Work out the following.
    a) $\frac{1}{6}$ of 38   **b)** $\frac{1}{3}$ of 38   **c)** $\frac{5}{6}$ of 38

6 Work out the following amounts exactly.
    a) $\frac{5}{8}$ of \$36.80   **b)** $\frac{1}{4}$ of \$25.68   **c)** $\frac{5}{9}$ of \$127.89

Adding and subtracting fractions and mixed numbers

For fractions to be either added or subtracted, the denominators need to be the same. If the denominators are different, the fractions need to be converted into equivalent fractions with a common denominator first.

Worked examples

a) Work out $\frac{3}{11} + \frac{5}{11}$.
$$\frac{3}{11} + \frac{5}{11} = \frac{8}{11}$$

b) Work out $\frac{7}{8} + \frac{5}{8}$.
$$\frac{7}{8} + \frac{5}{8} = \frac{12}{8}$$
$$= 1\frac{4}{8}$$
$$= 1\frac{1}{2}$$

c) Work out $1\frac{3}{4} + 2\frac{1}{2}$.
$$1\frac{3}{4} + 2\frac{1}{2} = 1 + 2 + \frac{3}{4} + \frac{1}{2}$$
$$= 3 + \frac{3}{4} + \frac{2}{4}$$
$$= 3 + \frac{5}{4}$$
$$= 3 + 1\frac{1}{4}$$
$$= 4\frac{1}{4}$$

d) Work out $\frac{4}{5} - \frac{3}{10}$.

$$\frac{4}{5} - \frac{3}{10} = \frac{8}{10} - \frac{3}{10}$$
$$= \frac{5}{10}$$
$$= \frac{1}{2}$$

e) Work out $5\frac{3}{8} - 2\frac{5}{8}$.

$$5\frac{3}{8} - 2\frac{5}{8} = \frac{43}{8} - \frac{21}{8}$$
$$= \frac{22}{8}$$
$$= 2\frac{6}{8}$$
$$= 2\frac{3}{4}$$

It is sometimes easier to change mixed numbers to improper fractions first.

EXERCISE 15.2B

Work out the following. Simplify your answers where possible.

1 a) $\frac{2}{3} + \frac{1}{3}$ **b)** $\frac{5}{9} + \frac{4}{9}$ **c)** $\frac{3}{7} + \frac{2}{7}$

   d) $\frac{5}{11} + \frac{4}{11}$ **e)** $\frac{1}{9} + \frac{1}{3}$ **f)** $\frac{1}{4} + \frac{3}{8}$

2 a) $\frac{9}{11} - \frac{3}{11}$ **b)** $\frac{4}{5} - \frac{1}{5}$ **c)** $\frac{8}{9} - \frac{4}{9}$

   d) $\frac{6}{13} - \frac{1}{13}$ **e)** $\frac{1}{3} - \frac{1}{9}$ **f)** $\frac{3}{4} - \frac{3}{8}$

3 a) $2\frac{2}{3} + 1\frac{1}{3}$ **b)** $3\frac{1}{4} + 1\frac{3}{4}$ **c)** $5\frac{1}{3} + 2\frac{1}{9}$

   d) $6\frac{1}{2} + 2\frac{3}{4}$ **e)** $7\frac{3}{10} - 3\frac{1}{10}$ **f)** $5\frac{1}{2} - 2\frac{3}{4}$

4 a) $\frac{3}{5} + \frac{4}{5}$ **b)** $\frac{3}{11} + \frac{7}{11}$ **c)** $\frac{2}{3} + \frac{1}{4}$

   d) $\frac{3}{9} + \frac{4}{9}$ **e)** $\frac{8}{13} + \frac{2}{5}$ **f)** $\frac{1}{2} + \frac{2}{3} + \frac{3}{4}$

5 a) $\frac{3}{7} - \frac{2}{7}$ **b)** $\frac{4}{5} - \frac{7}{10}$ **c)** $\frac{8}{9} - \frac{1}{3}$

   d) $\frac{7}{12} - \frac{1}{2}$ **e)** $\frac{5}{8} - \frac{2}{5}$ **f)** $\frac{3}{4} - \frac{2}{5} + \frac{7}{10}$

6 a) $2\frac{1}{2} + 3\frac{1}{4}$ **b)** $3\frac{3}{5} + 1\frac{7}{10}$ **c)** $3\frac{3}{5} - 2\frac{1}{5}$

   d) $5\frac{7}{8} - 3\frac{3}{8}$ **e)** $5\frac{7}{8} - 4\frac{3}{4}$ **f)** $3\frac{3}{4} - 2\frac{1}{2}$

Multiplying and dividing an integer by a fraction

If you multiply an integer by a fraction, the answer is often an improper fraction which can then be simplified.

Worked examples

a) Work out $3 \times \frac{3}{4}$.

$$3 \times \frac{3}{4} = \frac{9}{4} = 2\frac{1}{4}$$

b) Work out $5 \times \frac{3}{8}$.

$$5 \times \frac{3}{8} = \frac{15}{8} = 1\frac{7}{8}$$

c) Work out $6 \times \frac{5}{6}$.

$$6 \times \frac{5}{6} = \frac{30}{6} = 5$$

d) Work out $7 \times \frac{5}{14}$.

$$7 \times \frac{5}{14} = \frac{35}{14} = \frac{5}{2} = 2\frac{1}{2}$$

To divide by a fraction, remember that dividing by $\frac{1}{2}$ is the same as multiplying by 2. Similarly, dividing by $\frac{3}{8}$ is the same as multiplying by $\frac{8}{3}$.

Worked examples

a) Work out $3 \div \frac{3}{8}$.

$$3 \div \frac{3}{8} = 3 \times \frac{8}{3} = \frac{24}{3} = 8$$

b) Work out $5 \div \frac{3}{5}$.

$$5 \div \frac{3}{5} = 5 \times \frac{5}{3} = \frac{25}{3} = 8\frac{1}{3}$$

c) Work out $6 \div \frac{3}{7}$.

$$6 \div \frac{3}{7} = 6 \times \frac{7}{3} = \frac{42}{3} = 14$$

d) Work out $8 \div \frac{4}{5}$.

$$8 \div \frac{4}{5} = 8 \times \frac{5}{4} = \frac{40}{4} = 10$$

EXERCISE 15.2C

Work out the following. Simplify your answers where possible.

1 a) $3 \times \frac{2}{3}$ **b)** $5 \times \frac{3}{5}$ **c)** $8 \times \frac{7}{8}$

2 a) $6 \times \frac{5}{6}$ **b)** $9 \times \frac{7}{9}$ **c)** $11 \times \frac{9}{11}$

3 a) $6 \times \frac{2}{3}$ **b)** $10 \times \frac{3}{5}$ **c)** $16 \times \frac{7}{8}$

4 a) $12 \times \frac{2}{3}$ **b)** $25 \times \frac{3}{5}$ **c)** $24 \times \frac{7}{8}$

5 a) $6 \times \frac{3}{5}$ **b)** $7 \times \frac{3}{8}$ **c)** $2 \times \frac{4}{7}$

6 a) $8 \times \frac{3}{5}$ **b)** $6 \times \frac{3}{11}$ **c)** $9 \times \frac{7}{10}$

7 a) $3 \div \frac{3}{5}$ **b)** $5 \div \frac{5}{3}$ **c)** $8 \div \frac{8}{7}$

8 a) $10 \div \frac{10}{11}$ **b)** $9 \div \frac{3}{4}$ **c)** $18 \div \frac{6}{7}$

9 a) $8 \div \frac{4}{5}$ **b)** $16 \div \frac{4}{5}$ **c)** $24 \div \frac{6}{7}$

10 a) $36 \div \frac{9}{10}$ **b)** $42 \div \frac{7}{8}$ **c)** $64 \div \frac{8}{9}$

Percentages

Percentages, fractions and decimals are all different ways of representing values. The unique feature of percentages is that they are written as a fraction of 100.

You should already be familiar with the percentage equivalents of simple fractions and decimals as outlined in this table.

Fraction	Decimal	Percentage
$\frac{1}{2}$	0.5	50%
$\frac{1}{4}$	0.25	25%
$\frac{3}{4}$	0.75	75%
$\frac{1}{8}$	0.125	12.5%
$\frac{3}{8}$	0.375	37.5%
$\frac{5}{8}$	0.625	62.5%
$\frac{7}{8}$	0.875	87.5%
$\frac{1}{10}$	0.1	10%

Fraction	Decimal	Percentage
$\frac{2}{10}$ or $\frac{1}{5}$	0.2	20%
$\frac{3}{10}$	0.3	30%
$\frac{4}{10}$ or $\frac{2}{5}$	0.4	40%
$\frac{6}{10}$ or $\frac{3}{5}$	0.6	60%
$\frac{7}{10}$	0.7	70%
$\frac{8}{10}$ or $\frac{4}{5}$	0.8	80%
$\frac{9}{10}$	0.9	90%

Simple percentages

Worked examples

a) Of 100 sheep in a field, 83 are ewes.

    (i) What fraction, decimal and percentage of the sheep are ewes?

    (ii) What fraction, decimal and percentage are not ewes?

    (i) 83 out of 100 are ewes $= \frac{83}{100} = 0.83 = 83\%$

    (ii) 17 out of 100 are not ewes $= \frac{17}{100} = 0.17 = 17\%$

b) Convert 35% into a fraction and a decimal.

$$35\% = \frac{35}{100} = \frac{7}{20}$$

$$35\% = \frac{35}{100} = 0.35$$

EXERCISE 15.3A

1 In a survey of 100 cars, 45 were silver, 13 were blue and 30 were red. Express each of these numbers as a fraction, a decimal and a percentage of the total.

2 $\frac{3}{10}$ of the surface of the Earth is land. Express this as a decimal and a percentage.

3 There are 500 students in a school. 220 of them are female. What percentage of the school is:

a) female

b) male?

4 Write each of these percentages as a fraction in its simplest form.

a) 23%   **b)** 68%   **c)** 70%   **d)** 75%

5 Write each of these fractions as a percentage.

a) $\frac{49}{100}$ **b)** $\frac{9}{10}$ **c)** $\frac{17}{50}$ **d)** $\frac{3}{4}$

6 Convert each of these percentages to a decimal.

a) 69%   **b)** 87%   **c)** 83%

d) 3%   **e)** 102%   **f)** 220%

7 Convert each of these decimals to a percentage.

a) 0.61   **b)** 0.17   **c)** 0.89

d) 0.08   **e)** 1.25   **f)** 2.75

Calculating a percentage of a quantity

Worked example

A computer engineer earns $2500 per month. She decides to save 12% of her earnings and puts this money into her savings account. Calculate the amount of money she pays into her savings account each month.

Method 1: The unitary method

Let the $2500 be represented by 100%, as shown in this diagram.

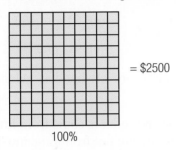

= $2500

100%

To work out 1% we must divide the quantity by 100.

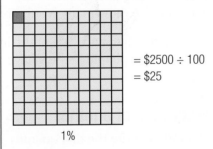

= $2500 ÷ 100
= $25

1%

Therefore 12% looks like this:

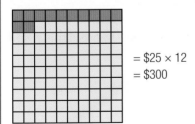

= $25 × 12
= $300

12%

> This method is called the **unitary method** because 1% is calculated first and then the result is multiplied by the required amount.

Therefore she puts $300 into her savings account each month.

Method 2: Decimal equivalence

12% can be converted to a decimal, i.e. 0.12.
Therefore 12% of $2500 is
$$0.12 \times \$2500 = \$300$$

EXERCISE 15.3B

Work out the following.

1 **a)** 10% of 60   **b)** 25% of 160   **c)** 60% of 150

2 **a)** 12.5% of 80   **b)** 37.5% of 80   **c)** 87.5% of 80

3 **a)** 46% of 50   **b)** 50% of 46   **c)** 23% of 50

4 **a)** 70% of 125   **b)** 7% of 125   **c)** 7% of 375

5 **a)** 12% of 180   **b)** 36% of 180   **c)** 60% of 180

6 **a)** 90% of 90   **b)** 9% of 90   **c)** 9% of 9

7 15% of students in a school of 720 students are left-handed. What number of students are right-handed?

8 At a Cambridge college, 65% of the maths students come from England. If there are 240 maths students, how many are not from England?

9 A survey showed that 75% of vehicles passing a school were cars. If 4200 vehicles passed the school in one day, how many were cars?

10 In a village of 3500 people, 12% are left-handed, and 15% of the left-handed people have blonde hair. How many people in the village are blonde and left-handed?

Expressing one quantity as a percentage of another

To write one quantity as a percentage of another, write the first quantity as a fraction of the second and then multiply by 100.

Worked examples

a) In an examination, a girl gets 35 marks out of 40. Express this result as a percentage.
$$\frac{35}{40} \times 100 = 87.5\%$$

The girl gets 87.5%.

b) In a music quiz, a boy gets 54 correct answers out of 75 questions. Write this result as a percentage.
$$\frac{54}{75} \times 100 = 72\%$$

The boy gets 72%.

EXERCISE 15.3C

In questions 1–5, write the first quantity as a percentage of the second.

1 **a)** 36 out of 72   **b)** 18 out of 90   **c)** 5 out of 20

2 **a)** 6 out of 60   **b)** 36 out of 60   **c)** 54 out of 60

3 **a)** 7 out of 70   **b)** 21 out of 70   **c)** 49 out of 70

4 **a)** 45 out of 900   **b)** 135 out of 900   **c)** 180 out of 900

5 **a)** 11 out of 44   **b)** 11 out of 440   **c)** 77 out of 440

6 A school football team plays 25 games in a season. They win 17, draw 2 and lose the rest. Express the numbers won, drawn and lost as percentages of the total number of games played.

7 An airline has a fleet of 80 planes. Of these, 10 are being serviced at any one time. What percentage of the fleet is available for flights?

8 A car manufacturer produces 175 000 sports cars a year. They are only available in white, black and red. 52 500 are white, 78 750 are black and the rest are red.
a) What percentage of the cars are black?
b) What percentage are white?
c) What percentage are red?

Percentage increase and decrease

If a quantity increases by 8% then it has increased from 100% to 108% of the original.

If a quantity decreases by 8% then it has decreased from 100% to 92% of the original.

EXERCISE 15.3D

Write the following percentage changes as a percentage of the original amount.

1 An increase of
    a) 20%   **b)** 50%   **c)** 3%

2 A decrease of
    a) 12%   **b)** 30%   **c)** 7%

To work out the new value after an increase or decrease, multiply the original value by the new percentage.

Worked examples

a) A saloon car priced at $25 000 is increased in price by 5%. What is the new price?
The new price is 105% of the old price.
Therefore the new price is 105% of $25 000.
105% can be written in decimal form as 1.05.
Therefore the new price is 1.05 × $25 000 = $26 250.

b) A shop is having a sale of computers.
If a computer priced at $800 is reduced by 20%, what is the sale price?
The new price is 80% of the original price.
Therefore the sale price is 80% of $800.
80% can be written in decimal form as 0.8.
Therefore the sale price is 0.8 × $800 = $640.

Reducing a price by 20% is also called giving a 20% discount.

EXERCISE 15.3E

1 Increase each of the following by the given percentage.
  a) 160 by 25%   **b)** 200 by 40%   **c)** 150 by 30%

2 Decrease each of the following by the given percentage.
  a) 240 by 25%   **b)** 300 by 20%   **c)** 250 by 30%

3 A farmer produced 8000 tonnes of grain last year. He plans to increase this by 15% next year. How many tonnes does he think he will produce?

4 A winter coat is priced at $250 but is discounted by 15% in a sale. What is the sale price?

5 A builder charges $2000 plus 15% tax to fit a new kitchen. What is the total price of fitting the kitchen?

6 A family sees the kitchen they want priced at $7200 but it is offered at a discount of 40% in a sale. What is the sale price?

7 A car cost $11 500 new but lost 35% of its value in the first three years. What is it worth after three years? *This loss in value is called **depreciation**.*

8 The car in question 7 loses a further 8% in the next year. What is it worth at the end of year 4?

16 Sequences, functions and graphs

◆ Generate terms of a linear sequence using term-to-term and position-to-term rules; find term-to-term and position-to-term rules of sequences, including spatial patterns.
◆ Use a linear expression to describe the nth term of a simple arithmetic sequence, justifying its form by referring to the activity or practical context from which it was generated.
◆ Express simple functions algebraically and represent them in mappings.
◆ Construct tables of values and use all four quadrants to plot the graphs of linear functions, where y is given explicitly in terms of x; recognise that equations of the form $y = mx + c$ correspond to straight-line graphs.

Sequences

A **sequence** is an ordered set of numbers. Each number in the sequence is called a **term**. The terms of a sequence form a pattern.

Below are examples of three different types of sequence.

● **2 4 6 8 10 12**

In this sequence we are adding 2 to each term in order to produce the next term.

● **1 2 4 8 16 32**

In this sequence we double each term in order to produce the next term.

● **1 4 9 16 25 36**

Here, the difference between consecutive terms increases by 2 each time. It is also the sequence of square numbers.

Sequences in diagrams

Sequences can also be expressed as a series of diagrams. The example below shows the first four diagrams in a sequence of tile patterns.

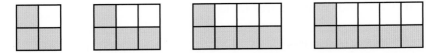

We can see that the tile patterns grow according to a rule.

We can enter the numbers of white and blue tiles in each pattern into a table of results.

Number of white tiles	1	2	3	4
Number of blue tiles	3	4	5	6

There are two types of rule which describe the sequence of blue tiles:

- The number of blue tiles increases by 1 each time. (This is known as a **term-to-term rule** as it describes how to get from one term to the next.)
- The number of blue tiles is always 2 more than the number of white tiles. (This is known as a **position-to-term rule** as it describes how to calculate the term from its position in the sequence.)

The second rule, linking the number of blue tiles to the number of white tiles, can be explained by looking at the patterns themselves.

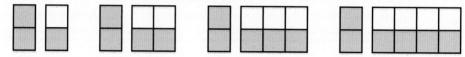

Each of the four patterns has been split in two. We can see that in the right-hand part of each pattern, the number of blue tiles is equal to the number of white tiles. The left-hand parts show 2 extra blue tiles being added each time. Therefore the number of blue tiles is always 2 more than the number of white tiles.

If we want to know how many blue tiles are needed for a pattern with 100 white tiles, the second rule helps us:

Number of blue tiles = number of white tiles + 2
Number of blue tiles = 100 + 2 = 102

EXERCISE 16.1

These diagrams show the first three patterns in a sequence of growing tile patterns.

1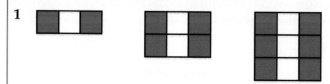

a) Draw the next two diagrams in the sequence.
b) Copy and complete this table.

Number of white tiles	1	2	3	4	5
Number of red tiles					

c) Describe the term-to-term rule for the number of red tiles.

d) Describe the position-to-term rule linking the number of white tiles to the number of red tiles.

e) Explain, using the patterns, why your position-to-term rule works.

f) Use your rule in part **d)** to predict the number of red tiles in a pattern with 100 white tiles.

2 a) Draw the next two diagrams in this sequence.

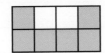 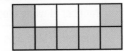

b) Copy and complete this table.

Number of white tiles	1	2	3	4	5
Number of green tiles					

c) Describe the term-to-term rule for the number of green tiles.

d) Describe the position-to-term rule linking the number of white tiles to the number of green tiles.

e) Explain, using the patterns, why your position-to-term rule works.

f) Use your rule in part **d)** to predict the number of green tiles in a pattern with 100 white tiles.

3 a) Draw the next two diagrams in this sequence.

b) Copy and complete this table.

Number of white tiles	1	2	3	4	5
Number of orange tiles					

c) Describe the term-to-term rule for the number of orange tiles.

d) Describe the position-to-term rule linking the number of white tiles to the number of orange tiles.

e) Explain, using the patterns, why your position-to-term rule works.

f) Use your rule in part **d)** to predict the number of orange tiles in a pattern with 100 white tiles.

➡

4 **a)** Draw the next two diagrams in this sequence.

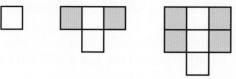

b) Copy and complete this table.

Number of white tiles	1	2	3	4	5
Number of blue tiles					

c) Describe the term-to-term rule for the number of blue tiles.
d) Describe the position-to-term rule linking the number of white tiles to the number of blue tiles.
e) Explain, using the patterns, why your position-to-term rule works.
f) Use your rule in part **d)** to predict the number of blue tiles in a pattern with 100 white tiles.

5 **a)** Draw the next two diagrams in this sequence.

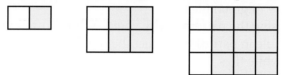

b) Copy and complete this table.

Number of white tiles	1	2	3	4	5
Number of yellow tiles					

c) Describe the term-to-term rule for the number of yellow tiles.
d) Describe the position-to-term rule linking the number of white tiles to the number of yellow tiles.
e) Explain, using the patterns, why your position-to-term rule works.
f) Use your rule in part **d)** to predict the number of yellow tiles in a pattern with 100 white tiles.

Term-to-term rules

A rule which describes how to get from one term to the next is called a **term-to-term** rule.

Worked examples

a) Here is a sequence of numbers.

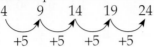

4   9   14   19   24

+5   +5   +5   +5

The term-to-term rule for this sequence is +5. What is the tenth term?
   To calculate the tenth term in the sequence, the pattern can be continued using the term-to-term rule:

   4 9 14 19 24   29 34 39 44 **49**

b) Here is a sequence of numbers.

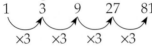

1   3   9   27   81

×3   ×3   ×3   ×3

The term-to-term rule for this sequence is ×3. What is the eighth term?
   To calculate the eighth term in the sequence, the pattern can be continued using the term-to-term rule:

   1   3   9   27   81   243   729   **2187**

EXERCISE 16.2A

For each of the sequences in questions 1–12:
a) describe the term-to-term rule
b) calculate the tenth term.

1 2 4 6 8 10   **2** 1 3 5 7 9

3 4 7 10 13 16   **4** 2 6 10 14 18

5 1 8 15 22 29   **6** 7 14 21 28 35

7 9 18 27 36 45   **8** 0.5 1 1.5 2 2.5

9 0.25 0.5 0.75 1 1.25   **10** 9 7 5 3 1

11 32 28 24 20 16   **12** 144 132 120 108

EXERCISE 16.2B

For each of the sequences in questions 1–10:
a) describe the term-to-term rule
b) calculate the tenth term.

1 3   6   12   24   48

2 1   3   7   15   31

3 32   16   8   4   2

4 1.1   0.9   0.7   0.5   0.3

5 $\frac{1}{2}$ $\frac{1}{3}$ $\frac{1}{4}$ $\frac{1}{5}$ $\frac{1}{6}$

6 $\frac{1}{2}$ $\frac{2}{3}$ $\frac{3}{4}$ $\frac{4}{5}$ $\frac{5}{6}$

7 1   4   9   16   25

8 4   7   12   19   28

9 1   8   27   64

10 5   25   125   625

The nth term

The method we have used to generate a sequence relies on knowing the previous term to work out the next one. The method works, but it takes a long time to work out the 100th term if only the first five terms are given! There is a more efficient method which is related to a term's position in the sequence, similar to the one used earlier with the tile patterns.

Worked examples

a) This table gives the first five terms of a sequence and their positions in the sequence.

Position	1	2	3	4	5
Term	4	8	12	16	20

Write down an expression for the nth term.
By looking at the sequence, we can see that each term is equal to its position number multiplied by 4.
The position number can be represented by the letter n.
Therefore the **nth term** for this sequence can be given by the expression $4n$.

b) This table gives the first five terms of a sequence and their positions in the sequence.

Position	1	2	3	4	5
Term	4	7	10	13	16

Write down an expression for the nth term.
By looking at the sequence we can see that each term is equal to 1 more than its position number multiplied by 3.
Using n to represent the position number, the nth term is given by the expression $3n + 1$.

EXERCISE 16.3A

For each of the sequences in questions 1–15:
a) write down the next two terms
b) write down an expression for the nth term.

1	3 5 7 9 11	
3	4 7 10 13 16	
5	5 9 13 17 21	
7	6 11 16 21 26	
9	8 15 22 29 36	
11	4 9 14 19 24	
13	0 4 8 12 16	
15	0 1 2 3 4	

2 4 6 8 10 12

4 5 8 11 14 17

6 7 11 15 19 23

8 9 14 19 24 29

10 9 19 29 39 49

12 1 8 15 22 29

14 1.5 3.5 5.5 7.5 9.5

The rule for the nth term can also be represented as a mapping. If, for example, the rule for the nth term of a sequence is given as $3n - 4$ the values can be shown in a table like this:

Position	1	2	3	4	5
Term	−1	2	5	8	11

They can also be shown as a mapping like this:

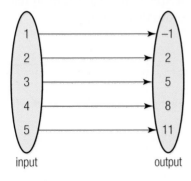

input   output

Each of the expressions in questions 1–8 gives a rule for the nth term of a sequence. Represent the first five terms of each sequence as a mapping.

1 $2n + 5$

2 $4n - 6$

3 $5n + 1$

4 $\frac{1}{2}n + 3$

5 $5 - 2n$

6 $8 - 6n$

7 $-n - 1$

8 $-3n + 4$

Linear graphs

As you learned in Student's Book 1, a line is made up of an infinite number of points. Plotted on a coordinate grid, the position of each point can be described using coordinates. For example,

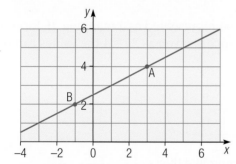

$A = (3, 4)$
$B = (-1, 2)$

The coordinates of every point on a straight line all have a common relationship, that is, there is a rule which the x and y coordinates follow.

The line opposite is plotted on a coordinate grid.

By putting the coordinates of some of the points in a table, we can see a pattern linking the x and y values.

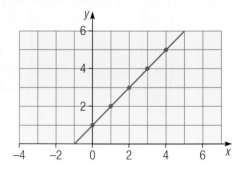

x	0	1	2	3	4
y	1	2	3	4	5

We can see that the y coordinates are always 1 more than the x coordinates. In algebra this can be written as $y = x + 1$. This is known as the **equation of the straight line** and simply describes the relationship between the x and y coordinates of all the points on the line.

EXERCISE 16.4A

For each of the straight lines shown in questions 1–8, write in a table the coordinates of five of the points on the line and deduce the equation of the line.

1

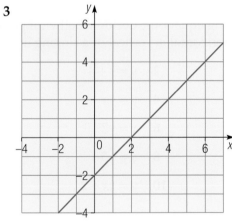

2

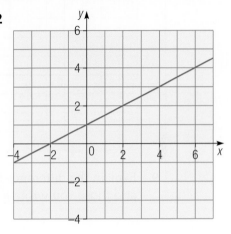

3

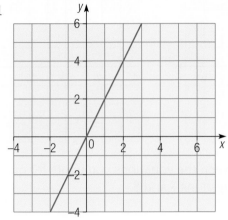

4

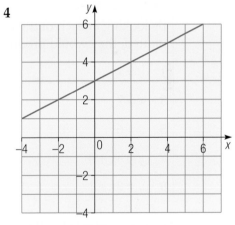

5

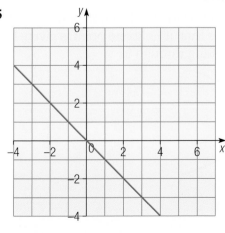

6

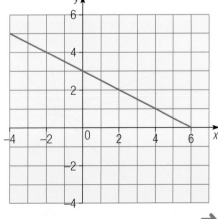

7

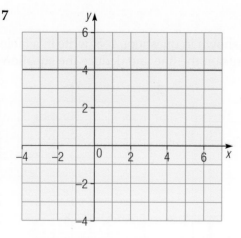

8

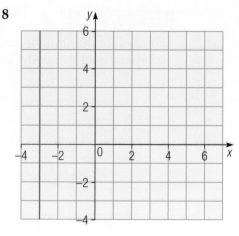

9 Explain the difference between the equations you wrote for questions 1–6 and those you wrote for questions 7 and 8.

By looking at each of the following equations, decide whether, if points were plotted, they would produce a horizontal, a vertical or a sloping line.

1 $y = x$

2 $y = x + 4$

3 $x = 7$

4 $y = -x$

5 $y = 6$

6 $x = -2$

7 $y = -x + 4$

8 $y = -3$

9 $y = 3x - 1$

10 $y = \frac{1}{2}x - 2$

Drawing straight-line graphs

To be able to draw a straight line, knowing the position of one point on the line is not enough. This diagram shows that, if only one point is given, then any number of lines can be drawn passing through it.

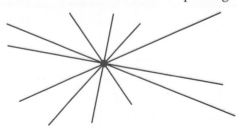

However, if the positions of two points are given, then only one line can pass through them both:

Therefore, to be able to draw a straight line from an equation, the positions of two points need to be calculated and plotted.

Worked example

Draw the line $y = 2x - 1$ on a coordinate grid.

To find the positions of two points on the line, choose two values for x. Substitute each of these into the equation and calculate the y value.

When $x = 0$, $y = -1$, giving the coordinates $(0, -1)$.
When $x = 3$, $y = 5$, giving the coordinates $(3, 5)$.

Plotting these two points and drawing the line between them gives the following graph.

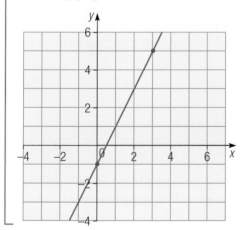

It is good practice to check a third point.

When $x = 1$, $y = 1$.

As the point $(1, 1)$ lies on the line, the graph is correct.

EXERCISE 16.4C

On a coordinate grid, draw the straight line represented by each of these equations.

First identify the coordinates of three points on the line.

1 $y = x + 2$

2 $y = 2x - 3$

3 $y = \frac{1}{2}x + 1$

4 $y = 3$

5 $y = x - 1$

6 $x = -2$

7 $y = \frac{1}{2}x + 3$

8 $y = -x + 3$

9 $y = -2x + 2$

10 $y = -x - 1$

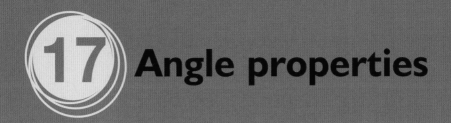

17 Angle properties

◆ Identify alternate angles and corresponding angles.
◆ Understand a proof that:
  – the angle sum of a triangle is 180° and that of a quadrilateral is 360°
  – the exterior angle of a triangle is equal to the sum of the two interior opposite angles.
◆ Solve geometrical problems using properties of angles, of parallel and intersecting lines, and of triangles and special quadrilaterals, explaining reasoning with diagrams and text.

Alternate and corresponding angles

In Student's Book 1 you investigated the relationships between angles at a point on a straight line, around a point, and between intersecting lines.

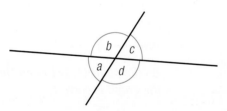

You saw that angles at a point on a straight line add up to 180°. In the diagram above, for example, $a + b = 180°$. They are called **supplementary** angles.

You also saw that angles around a point add up to 360°, for example $a + b + c + d = 360°$, and that **vertically opposite** angles are equal in size, for example $a = c$.

In addition, you were introduced to two further relationships between the angles formed within parallel and intersecting lines.

In the diagram below, angles a and g are equal. They are called **alternate** angles. Alternate angles can be found by looking for a 'Z' formation in a diagram.

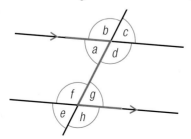

In this diagram, angles *a* and *e* are equal. They are called **corresponding** angles. Corresponding angles can be found by looking for an 'F' formation within a diagram.

The angles *b* and *f* are another pair of corresponding angles, so *b* = *f*. We know that *a* + *b* = 180°, so it follows that *a* + *f* = 180° and that angles *a* and *f* are **supplementary**.

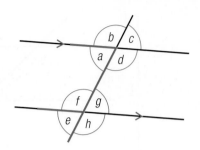

EXERCISE 17.1A

Use this diagram for questions 1–5.

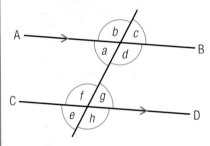

1 Write down as many pairs of angles as you can which add up to 180° because they are angles on a straight line.

2 Write down as many groups of angles as you can which add up to 360° because they are angles around a point.

3 Write down as many pairs of supplementary angles as you can.

4 Write down as many pairs of vertically opposite angles as you can.

5 Write down as many pairs of alternate angles as you can.

6 Write down as many pairs of corresponding angles as you can.

EXERCISE 17.1B

Calculate the size of each of the unknown angles in these diagrams. Give reasons for your answers.

1

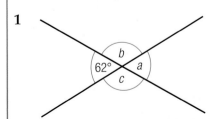

2

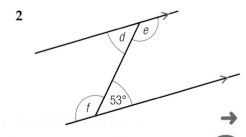

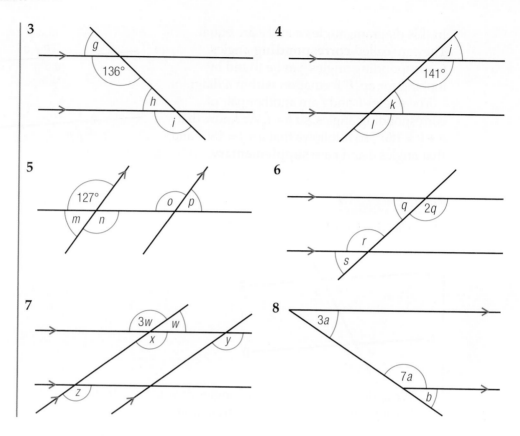

Angles and triangles

A triangle has three angles as shown.
   Although the sizes of the individual angles can vary, their total is always constant. The three angles always add up to 180°. In this triangle, for example,

$$a + b + c = 180°$$

We can prove this by drawing a line parallel to the base of the triangle and passing through its apex (highest point).

$c + d + e = 180°$ (angles on a straight line add up to 180°)

But $a = d$ (alternate angles are equal)

and $b = e$ (alternate angles are equal)

Therefore $c + d + e = a + b + c = 180°$

So the angles of a triangle always add up to 180°.

Worked example

This triangle is isosceles. Calculate the size of each of the
base angles from the information given.

$x + y + 40° = 180°$ (angles of a triangle add up to 180°)
$x + y = 180° - 40° = 140°$
But $x = y$ (base angles of an isosceles
triangle are equal)

Therefore $x = y = 70°$.

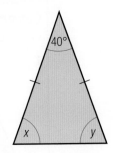

The **exterior angle** of a triangle is also related to the interior angles. An exterior
angle is found by extending one of the sides of the triangle. In this diagram,
angle d is an exterior angle.

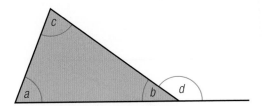

We already know that:

$a + b + c = 180°$ (angles of a triangle add up to 180°)

and that:

$b + d = 180°$ (angles on a straight line add up to 180°)

As the right-hand side of each equation is 180°, the left-hand sides must be
equal to each other too, that is:

$a + b + c = b + d$

Subtracting b from each side gives:

$a + c = d$

In other words, the exterior angle of a triangle is equal to the sum of the two
interior opposite angles.

Worked example

Calculate the size of angle x in this diagram.

$65° + x = 110°$ (exterior angle of a triangle
is equal to the sum of the
two interior opposite angles)

Therefore $x = 110° - 65° = 45°$.

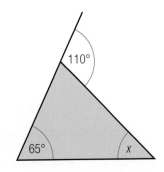

EXERCISE 17.2

Calculate the size of each of the unknown angles in these diagrams.
Give reasons for your answers.

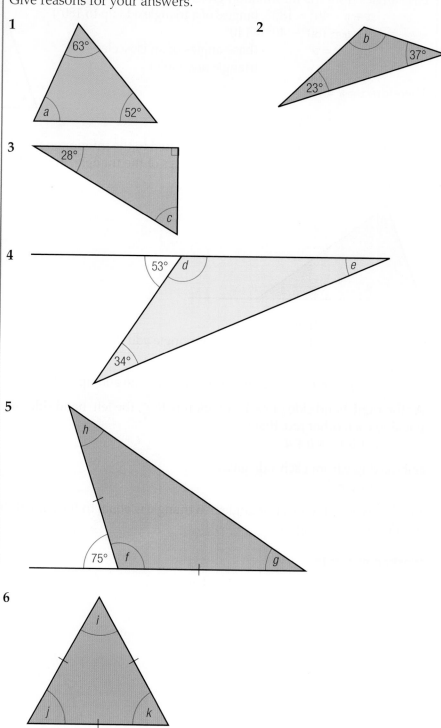

1

63°

a   52°

2

b

37°

23°

3

28°

c

4

53° d   e

34°

5

h

75° f   g

6

i

j   k

Angles of a quadrilateral

A quadrilateral has four angles as shown.

   As with triangles, the sizes of the individual angles can vary, but the sum of the four angles is the same for any quadrilateral. The four angles always add up to 360°. In this quadrilateral, for example,

$$p + q + r + s = 360°$$

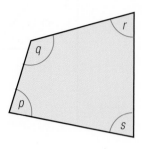

We can prove this by splitting the quadrilateral into two triangles.

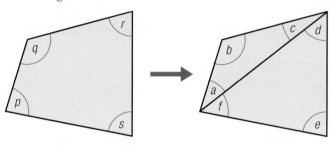

$a + b + c = 180°$ (angles of a triangle equal 180°)
$d + e + f = 180°$ (angles of a triangle equal 180°)

Therefore

    $a + b + c + d + e + f = 360°$ (sum of the angles of two triangles)

But $a + f = p$, $b = q$, $c + d = r$ and $e = s$, so

    $a + b + c + d + e + f = p + q + r + s$

Therefore the sum of the angles of any quadrilateral is 360°.

EXERCISE 17.3A

Calculate the size of each of the unknown angles in these diagrams. Give reasons for your answers.

1

2

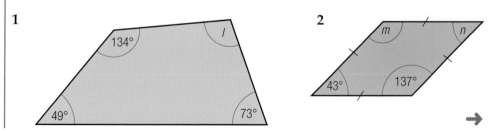

3

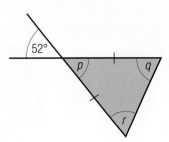

4

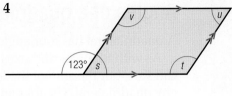

For questions 1–3, calculate the size of each of the unknown angles in the diagram.

Give reasons for your answers.

1

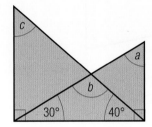

2

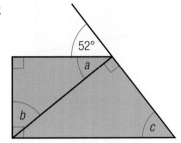

3

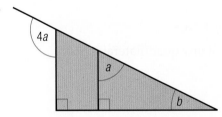

4 Calculate the size of each of the internal angles of this kite.

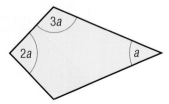

18 Area and volume

◆ Derive and use formulae for the area of a triangle, parallelogram and trapezium; calculate areas of compound two-dimensional shapes, and lengths, surface areas and volumes of cuboids.
◆ Know the definition of a circle and the names of its parts; know and use formulae for the circumference and area of a circle.

Rectangles

The area of a plane shape is the amount of two-dimensional (flat) space that it occupies. In Student's Book 1 you studied the areas of squares and rectangles. To find the area of a square or rectangle, the length and width are multiplied together.

Area = length × width

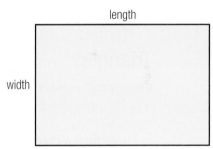

EXERCISE 18.1

1 Calculate the area of each of these rectangles.

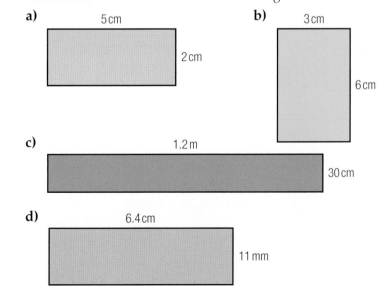

a) 5 cm, 2 cm

b) 3 cm, 6 cm

c) 1.2 m, 30 cm

d) 6.4 cm, 11 mm

2 Calculate the area of each of these rectangles.
Write the units of your answer clearly.
a) length = 12 cm width = 4 cm
b) length = 3.8 m width = 10 m
c) length = 3.2 cm width = 4.7 m
d) length = 85 cm width = 1.2 m
e) length = 3.3 m   width = 75 mm

3 Use the formula for the area of a rectangle to work out the missing values in this table.

	Length	Width	Area
a)	8.5 cm	7.2 cm	
b)	25 cm		250 cm²
c)		25 cm	400 cm²
d)		7.5 cm	187.5 cm²

Triangles

One of the angles of this triangle is a right angle; this is a right-angled triangle.

Drawing a rectangle around the triangle will help us to work out the formula for the area of a triangle.

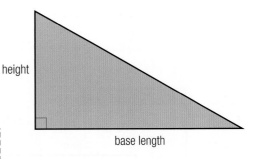

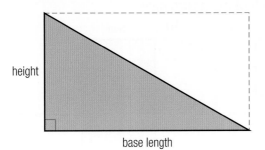

Area of rectangle = base length × height.

The area of the triangle is half the area of the rectangle.

Area of triangle = $\frac{1}{2}$ × base length × height

This also works for other triangles.

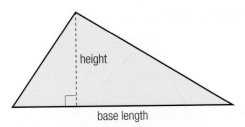

> *The height is always measured at right angles to the base. This is sometimes known as the **perpendicular height**.*

When we draw a rectangle around the triangle, we can see that the area of the triangle is still half that of the rectangle.

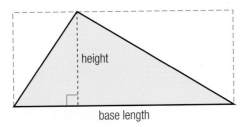

Area of a triangle = $\frac{1}{2}$ × base length × perpendicular height

There will be times when the base of the triangle is not conveniently given as a horizontal side. However, we can use *any* side of the triangle as the base. We must make sure, though, that we measure the height at right angles to the side chosen as the base. These diagrams demonstrate this.

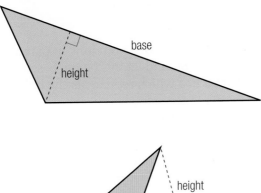

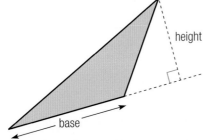

EXERCISE 18.2A

1 Calculate the area of each of these triangles.

a)

3 cm

4 cm

b)

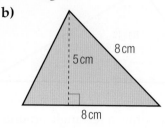

5 cm

8 cm

8 cm

c)

10 cm

11 cm

2 a) Draw a triangle similar to this one.

C

B

A

    (i) Measure the length of side *AB* and let this be the base of the triangle.

    (ii) Draw on your diagram a line which represents the height of the triangle.

    (iii) Measure the height of your triangle.

    (iv) Calculate the area of your triangle.

b) Draw another triangle *identical* to the one you drew in part **a)**.

    (i) Measure the length of side *BC* and let this be the base of the triangle.

    (ii) Draw on your diagram a line which represents the height of the triangle.

    (iii) Measure the height of your triangle.

    (iv) Calculate the area of your triangle.

c) Draw another triangle *identical* to the ones you drew in parts **a)** and **b)**.

    (i) Measure the length of side *AC* and let this be the base of the triangle.

    (ii) Draw on your diagram a line which represents the height of the triangle.

    (iii) Measure the height of your triangle.

    (iv) Calculate the area of your triangle.

d) What do you notice about the areas of the three triangles you drew? Comment carefully on the reasons for any differences or similarities in your answers.

3 Use the formula for the area of a triangle to work out the missing values in this table.

	Base length	Perpendicular height	Area
a)	7.2 cm	4.8 cm	
b)	20 cm		100 cm²
c)		15 cm	15 cm²
d)		11 cm	55 cm²

EXERCISE 18.2B

1 Calculate the area of each of these shapes.

a)

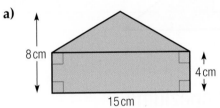

b)

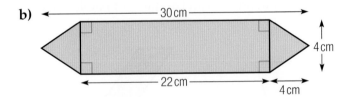

c)

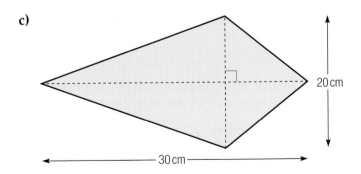

2 Calculate the area of the coloured region of each of these shapes.

a)

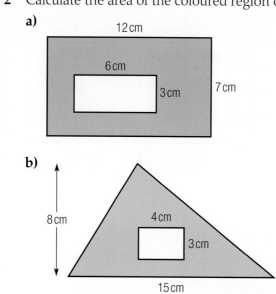

b)

Parallelograms and trapeziums

A parallelogram is a quadrilateral with two pairs of parallel sides. Here are two examples.

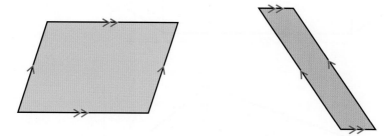

We use arrows to show that sides are parallel to one another.

To work out a rule for the area of a parallelogram, look at this parallelogram.

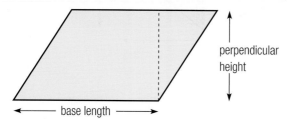

We can move the triangle on the right to the left-hand side of the parallelogram to make a rectangle.

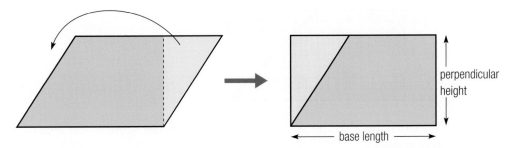

From the second diagram we can see that the base length and height of the parallelogram are exactly the same as those of the rectangle. Therefore they must have the same area.

Area of a parallelogram = base length × perpendicular height

As with a triangle, the height must always be measured at right angles to the base.

A trapezium is also a quadrilateral. It has only one pair of parallel sides. Here are some examples.

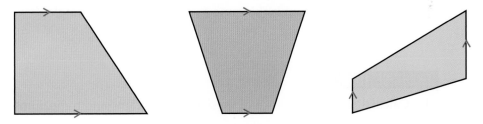

To work out a formula for calculating the area of a trapezium, look at this trapezium.

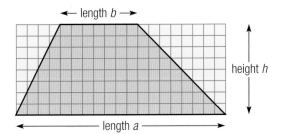

Length a and length b are the lengths of the two parallel sides.
   The height, h, of the trapezium is the perpendicular distance between the two

parallel sides.
We can draw a rectangle on the trapezium like this.

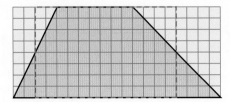

We can show that the area of the trapezium is the same as the area of the rectangle.

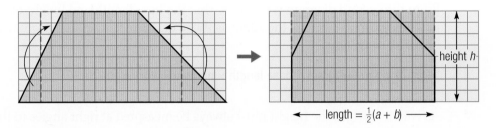

length = $\frac{1}{2}(a + b)$

The height of the rectangle is the same as the height of the trapezium.
The length of the rectangle is the *mean* of the lengths of the two parallel sides.
The area of the trapezium is the same as the area of the rectangle.

   Area of a trapezium = $\frac{1}{2}(a + b)h$

EXERCISE 18.3A

1   Calculate the area of each of these parallelograms and trapeziums.

a)

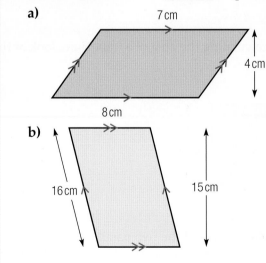

7 cm

4 cm

8 cm

b)

16 cm

15 cm

c)

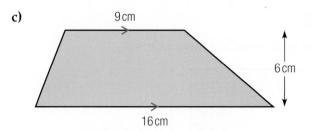

d)

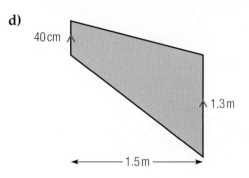

2 Use the formula for the area of a parallelogram to work out the missing values in this table.

	Length	Height	Area
a)	4 cm	8 cm	
b)	45 cm	0.2 m	
c)	30 cm		150 cm²
d)		0.45 m	45 cm²
e)		250 cm	1 m²

3 Use the formula for the area of a trapezium to work out the missing values in this table.

	Length *a*	Length *b*	Height	Area
a)	3 cm	8 cm	4 cm	
b)	20 cm	0.3 m	0.25 m	
c)	10 cm	20 cm		500 cm²
d)	0.25 m		40 cm	1100 cm²
e)		45 cm	0.04 m	150 cm²

EXERCISE 18.3B

1 Calculate the area of each of these shapes.

a)

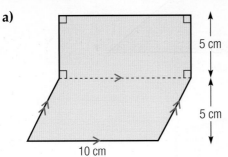

b)

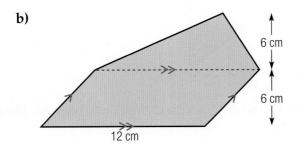

2 The area of the parallelogram in this diagram is 40 cm².
The area of the triangle and the area of the parallelogram are equal.
The area of the trapezium is twice the area of the triangle.
Calculate the missing dimensions.

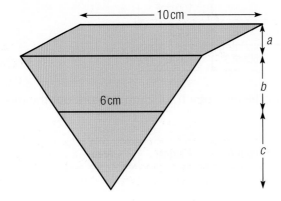

3 This rectangular graden is split into four sections. Sections *A* and *D* are trapeziums; sections *B* and *C* are triangles. The area of section *A* is twice that of section *B*.

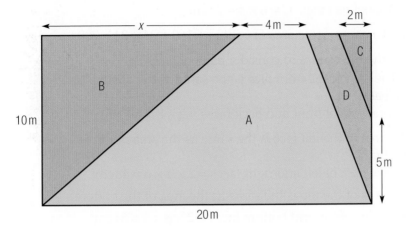

Showing your working clearly, calculate:
a) the area of the whole garden
b) the area of section *A*
c) the area of section *B*
d) the length of the side marked *x*
e) the area of section *C*
f) the area of section *D*.

Cuboids

The **surface area** of a cuboid is the total area of its six faces. In Student's Book 1 this was calculated by two methods. One method considered the net of the cuboid. For example,

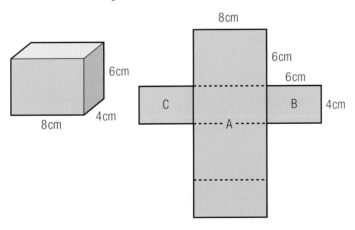

As each face is rectangular, the area of the net can be calculated like this:
    Area of large rectangle A = 8 × (6 + 4 + 6 + 4) = 8 × 20 = 160 cm²
    Area of rectangle B = 6 × 4 = 24 cm²
    Area of rectangle C = 6 × 4 = 24 cm²

Total area = surface area of cuboid = 160 + 24 + 24 = 208 cm²

Another method is to consider pairs of faces.

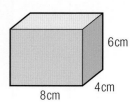

    The area of the front face is the same as the area of the back face.
    Total area of front and back faces = 2 × 8 × 6 = 96 cm²

The area of the left face is the same as the area of the right face.
    Total area of left and right faces = 2 × 4 × 6 = 48 cm²

The area of the top is the same as the area of the bottom.

Total area of top and bottom faces = 2 × 8 × 4 = 64 cm²

Total area = surface area of cuboid = 96 + 48 + 64 = 208 cm²

The **volume** of a cuboid is calculated simply by multiplying its three dimensions together.

> **Volume of a cuboid = length × width × height**

The volume of the cuboid above is calculated as 8 × 4 × 6 = 192 cm³.

EXERCISE 18.4

1 For the cuboid shown on the right, calculate:
    a) its volume
    b) its surface area.

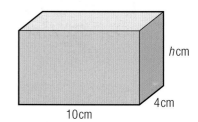

2 A cuboid has length 1 cm, width 2 cm and height 8 cm. Calculate:
    a) its volume
    b) its surface area.

3 The volume of this cuboid is 200 cm³. Calculate:
    a) its height h
    b) its surface area.

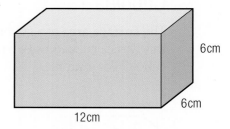

4 The total surface area of this cube is 216 cm². Calculate:
   a) the length x of each side
   b) the volume of the cube.

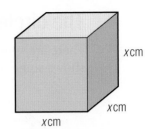

x cm

x cm

x cm

5 This cuboid has a pair of square faces, with edge lengths p cm. The total volume of the cuboid is 375 cm³. Calculate:
   a) the value of p
   b) the surface area of the cuboid.

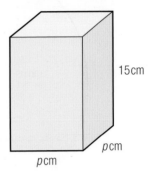

15 cm

p cm

p cm

6 The dimensions of cuboid B are double those of cuboid A as shown.

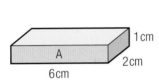

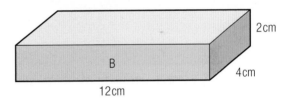

A

1 cm

2 cm

6 cm

B

2 cm

4 cm

12 cm

   a) Calculate the surface area of cuboid A.
   b) Calculate the surface area of cuboid B.
   c) How many times bigger is the surface area of B than that of A?
   d) Calculate the volume of cuboid A.
   e) Calculate the volume of cuboid B.
   f) How many times bigger is the volume of B than that of A?

7 The dimensions of a cuboid are as shown.
   a) Write an expression for the surface area of the cuboid in terms of a.
   b) The surface area is 1000 cm². Calculate the value of a.
   c) Calculate the volume of the cuboid.

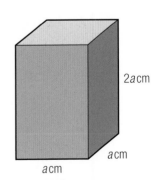

$2a$ cm

a cm

a cm

8 **a)** Write an expression for the volume of this cuboid in terms of x.
   b) The volume of the cuboid is 10 290 cm³. Calculate the value of x.
   c) Calculate the surface area of the cuboid.

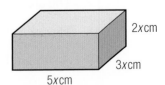

$2x$ cm

$3x$ cm

$5x$ cm

The circle

There are special words to describe different parts of a circle. The diagram below shows some of the main parts of the circle and gives their names.

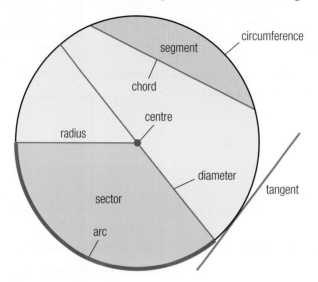

EXERCISE 18.5A

Copy and complete these sentences to give the definitions of the terms shown in the diagram above.

1   A line that is always the same distance from a single fixed point is called a _____.

2   The perimeter of a circle is called its _____.

3   A straight line from the centre of a circle to the circumference of the circle is called a _____. The plural of the word is _____.

4   A straight line across a circle which starts and ends at two points on the circumference is called a _____.

5   A chord which passes through the centre of a circle is called a _____.

6   A line which forms part of the circumference of a circle is called an _____.

7   The area enclosed by two radii and an arc is called a _____.

8   The area enclosed by an arc and a chord is called a _____.

9   A straight line which touches the circumference of a circle is called a _____.

Circumference of a circle

We saw on page 174 that the circumference of a circle is its perimeter, that is, the distance around the outside of the circle. In order to calculate the circumference of a circle, you can use a formula. However, here is a simple practical task which will help you deduce an approximate formula for the circumference of a circle.

Practical activity

You will need:
- a range of different-sized cylindrical objects
- a length of string
- a ruler
- paper and pencil (to record your results).
- Use a ruler to measure the diameter of each cylinder.

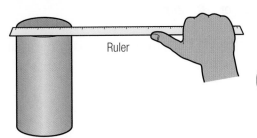

Ruler

For thin cylinders, this method may produce large inaccuracies. Discuss with a partner any strategies you could use to improve the accuracy of your results.

- Wrap string around each cylinder to measure its circumference.

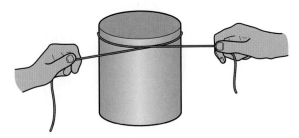

- Record your results for each cylinder in a table similar to this.

Cylindrical object	Circumference (cm)	Diameter (cm)

- Try to spot a pattern in your results, and find a rule linking the length of the circumference to the length of the diameter.

Because of experimental errors, your rule will only be approximate.

You will have seen from your results in the activity on page 175 that the length of the circumference of any circle is approximately three times the length of its diameter. In fact, the circumference is always the diameter multiplied by a constant value known as **pi** (π).

Pi is not an exact number; it has an infinite number of decimal places.
To two decimal places, π = 3.14
To 14 decimal places, π = 3.141 592 653 589 79
Therefore the circumference of any circle is given by the formula:

Circumference = π × diameter   or   C = πD

As the diameter is twice the radius, the circumference of a circle can also be given as:

Circumference = π × 2 × radius   or   C = 2πr

Scientific calculators have a $\boxed{\pi}$ key. Check to see how many decimal places your calculator gives pi to.

1 Calculate the circumference of each of these circles. The diameter of each circle has been given. Give your answers correct to two decimal places.

a)
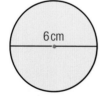
6 cm

b)
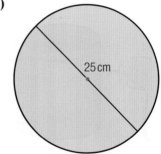
25 cm

c)

40 mm

d)
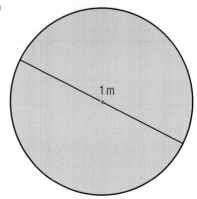
1 m

2   Calculate the circumference of each of these circles. The radius of each
    circle has been given. Give your answers correct to two decimal places.

a)

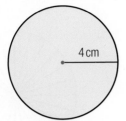

4 cm

b)

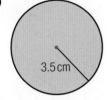

3.5 cm

c)

12 mm

d)

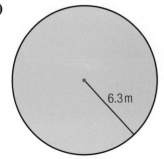

6.3 m

Area of a circle

The area of a circle can also be calculated using a formula. To show how the formula is deduced, look at these diagrams.

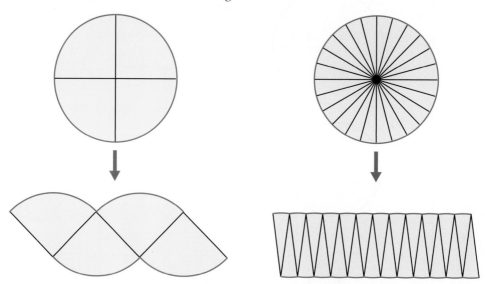

Each of the diagrams shows a circle split into sectors. In the first diagram, the circle has been divided into four sectors; in the second diagram the circle has been split into 24 sectors. The sectors are then rearranged to form another shape. As the number of sectors increases, the rearranged shape looks more and more like a rectangle. In theory therefore, if the circle was divided into an infinite number of sectors, then the rearranged shape would be a rectangle, as shown here.

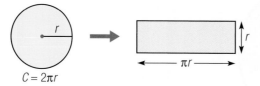

Note the following important points:

- The area of the rectangle and the area of the circle are the same. Therefore calculating the area of the rectangle will also give the area of the circle.
- The radius of the circle is the same as the width (height) of the rectangle.
- The length of the rectangle is half the circumference of the circle.

It follows that:

Area of the circle = area of the rectangle

$$= \text{length} \times \text{width}$$
$$= \pi r \times r$$
$$= \pi r^2$$

Area of a circle = πr^2

EXERCISE 18.5C

Calculate the area of each of these circles. Give your answers correct to one decimal place.

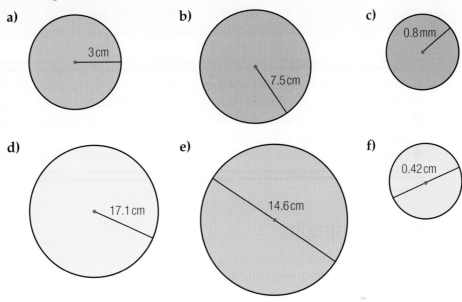

a) 3 cm

b) 7.5 cm

c) 0.8 mm

d) 17.1 cm

e) 14.6 cm

f) 0.42 cm

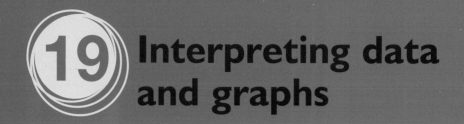

Interpreting data and graphs

19

◆ Interpret tables, graphs and diagrams for discrete and continuous data, and draw conclusions, relating statistics and findings to the original question.
◆ Compare two distributions, using the range and one or more of the mode, median and mean.
◆ Compare proportions in two pie charts that represent different totals.

Data and graphs

You are already familiar with many ways of recording and displaying data, including tables, frequency charts, pie charts, line graphs and stem-and-leaf diagrams.

As well as presenting data, however, it is also important to be able to interpret it. This means understanding what the data shows.

Worked example

The wingspans (in centimetres) of male and female adult birds of a particular species are given in this table.

Wingspan (cm)	Frequency	
	Male	Female
$10 \leqslant w < 10.5$	3	8
$10.5 \leqslant w < 11$	4	10
$11 \leqslant w < 11.5$	10	8
$11.5 \leqslant w < 12$	9	4
$12 \leqslant w < 12.5$	4	0

a) Show both sets of data on a frequency graph.
b) What is the modal wingspan for:
   (i) the male birds
   (ii) the female birds?
c) Another bird of the same species is caught. Its wingspan is 11.8 cm. Is it possible to decide whether it is male or female from this information?

a)

Wingspans of male and female birds

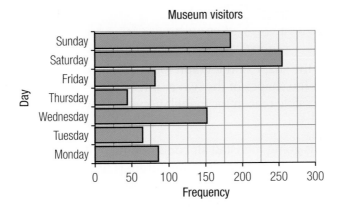

b) The modal group is the group with the highest frequency.
   (i) The modal wingspan for the male birds is $11\,\text{cm} \leqslant w < 11.5\,\text{cm}$.
   (ii) The modal wingspan for the female birds is $10.5\,\text{cm} \leqslant w < 11\,\text{cm}$.

c) It is not possible to decide for certain, as this wingspan is within both of the ranges. However, it is more likely to be male than female.

EXERCISE 19.1

1 The bar chart below shows the numbers of people visiting a small museum each day during one week.

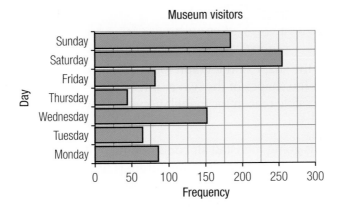

a) Give a possible reason why Saturday has the most visitors.
b) The museum is open for longer on one of the weekdays than on the other days. Which weekday is it likely to be? Give a reason for your answer.

→

2 A conservation group has studied the population of a particular mammal over a 50-year period. They are worried that the numbers are decreasing and survey the population every five years. The results of their survey are shown in the table below.

Year	1960	1965	1970	1975	1980	1985	1990	1995	2000	2005	2010
Population (1000s)	46	50	40	35	32	24	30	26	25	22	35

a) Draw a line graph for the data.

b) By commenting on the shape of your graph, decide whether the conservationists' concern is valid or not.

3 The numbers of rabbits and foxes in a national park are counted each year. Their numbers are shown in the line graphs below.

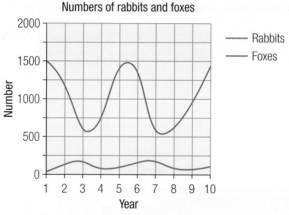

a) Describe the shape of the graph for the rabbits.

b) Compare the shapes of the two graphs.

c) Give a possible reason for the relationship between the shapes of the two graphs.

4 A company is going to install air conditioning in its offices. It will only be switched on when the outside temperature is higher than 28 °C. To estimate how much it will cost to operate, the outside temperature is recorded every four hours over a two-day period. The results are shown in the table below.

	Day 1						Day 2					
Time	0000	0400	0800	1200	1600	2000	0000	0400	0800	1200	1600	2000
Temperature (°C)	16	14	20	32	35	25	17	16	22	30	34	25

a) Draw a line graph showing the temperature over the two days.
b) Use your graph to estimate the times on the first day when the outside temperature was 28 °C.
c) Estimate how long the temperature was higher than 28 °C on the first day.
d) Estimate how long the temperature was higher than 28 °C on the second day.

5   Two classes take the same maths test, which is marked out of 10. One class is set by ability, and the other is a mixed ability class. These two graphs show the results for each of the classes.

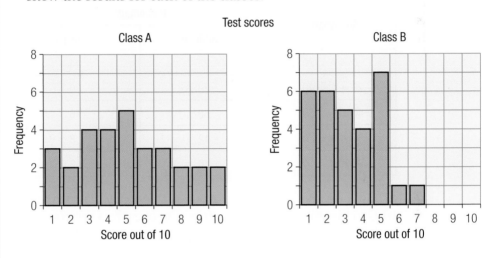

Test scores

a) What is the modal score for each class?
b) What is the range of scores for each class?
c) Which class is likely to be the class which is set by ability? Explain your answer.

6   Two types of light bulb are tested. 30 of each type are tested to see how long they last. The table shows the number of years the bulbs of each type last.

Number of years	Frequency	
	Type A	Type B
1	3	12
2	5	8
3	4	5
4	4	2
5	6	2
6	5	0
7	3	1

a) Calculate the mean, median and modal lifetime for each type of bulb.
b) Calculate the range in lifetime for each type of bulb.
c) An unmarked bulb is also tested and is found to last for seven years. Which type of bulb is it likely to be? Explain your answer.
d) The manufacturer of type A bulbs claims that 'on average' their bulbs last five times longer than those of type B. Is this claim true? Explain your answer.

7   This table shows the age distributions, by percentage of the population, of two countries.

Age (years)	Percentage	
	Country A	Country B
$0 \leqslant A < 20$	23	44
$20 \leqslant A < 40$	29	30
$40 \leqslant A < 60$	30	16
$60 \leqslant A < 80$	12	8
$80 \leqslant A < 100$	6	2

a) On the same axes, draw a grouped frequency diagram for each country.
b) Describe the population distribution of each of the countries.
c) What is the modal group for each country?
d) In which age group is the median age for each country?
e) One of the countries is from the developed world and one is from the developing world. Which country is likely to be from the developing world?
f) Give reasons for your answer to part e).

8   Two beach resorts (X and Y) want to advertise how much sun they have during August. One resort is in England, the other in Egypt. The table below shows the temperature at noon on alternate days during August in each resort.

Day	2	4	6	8	10	12	14	16	18	20	22	24	26	28	30
Noon temperature in resort X (°C)	28	27	25	25	29	31	26	26	27	25	25	30	33	25	24
Noon temperature in resort Y (°C)	37	37	36	36	40	38	37	37	39	42	35	37	33	34	44

a) Calculate the range, mean, median and mode of the temperatures for each resort.
b) Which resort is likely to be in Egypt? Give reasons for your answer.

Comparing pie charts

You saw in Chapter 5 that pie charts are an effective way of displaying data. Given a set of data displayed as a pie chart, it is important to be able make deductions from it.

For example, this pie chart shows the results of a survey of 36 students. They were asked whether they find maths easy, hard or OK.

From the pie chart we can see that most of these students find maths OK whilst the smallest number find it hard.

Another group of students were asked the same question. This pie chart shows their responses.

Looking at the two pie charts, it is easy to see that a smaller fraction of this group of students found maths OK than in the first group. But it is not so easy to compare the fractions who found it hard. There are more students (48) in the second group than in the first group (36) so we cannot just compare the numbers on the sectors. To be able to compare the data in the two pie charts, we need to use a common scale. For example, we can use percentages. The percentages for the first group are worked out in this table.

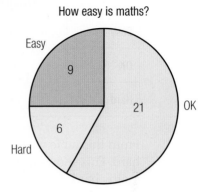

How easy is maths?

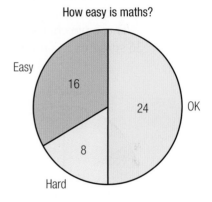

How easy is maths?

Group 1

	Frequency	Fraction of total	Percentage
Easy	9	$\frac{9}{36}$	$\frac{9}{36} \times 100 = 25\%$
OK	21	$\frac{21}{36}$	$\frac{21}{36} \times 100 = 58\%$
Hard	6	$\frac{6}{36}$	$\frac{6}{36} \times 100 = 17\%$

We can see that 17% of the students in this group find maths hard.

The percentage table produced from the pie chart for the second group is shown on page 186.

Group 2

	Frequency	Fraction of total	Percentage
Easy	16	$\frac{16}{48}$	$\frac{16}{48} \times 100 = 33\%$
OK	24	$\frac{24}{48}$	$\frac{24}{48} \times 100 = 50\%$
Hard	8	$\frac{8}{48}$	$\frac{8}{48} \times 100 = 17\%$

From this table we can see that 17% of the students in this group also find maths hard. This shows us that the same percentage of students in each group find maths hard.

In order to compare pie charts with different totals, it is helpful to convert the frequency of each category into a percentage.

These pie charts show the favourite sports of Group A and Group B. There are 36 students in Group A, and 30 students in Group B.

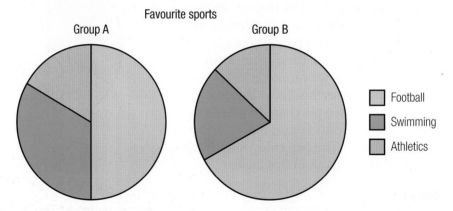

Looking at the pie charts you can see that football is the most popular sport in both groups. But to find out how many students prefer football you will need to measure the angle and work out the fraction of each compared with the full circle. Remember that there are 360° in a full circle.

The frequencies for Group A are worked out in this table.

Group A

	Angle	Fraction of total	Frequency
Football	180°	$\frac{180}{360}$	$\frac{180}{360} \times 36 = 18$
Swimming	120°	$\frac{120}{360}$	$\frac{120}{360} \times 36 = 12$
Athletics	60°	$\frac{60}{360}$	$\frac{60}{360} \times 36 = 6$

We can see that 18 students in Group A preferred football.

Here is the table for the second group.

Group B

	Angle	Fraction of total	Frequency
Football	241°	$\frac{241}{360}$	$\frac{241}{360} \times 30 = 20$
Swimming	72°	$\frac{72}{360}$	$\frac{72}{360} \times 30 = 6$
Athletics	47°	$\frac{47}{360}$	$\frac{47}{360} \times 30 = 4$

From this table we can see that 20 students in Group B preferred football.

EXERCISE 19.2

1 The hair colours of two groups of students are shown in the pie charts below.

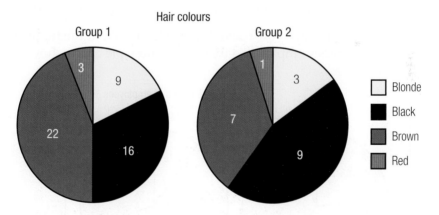

Hair colours

a) Which group had the highest number of students with black hair?
b) Which group had the highest percentage of students with black hair? Show your working clearly.
c) What is the difference in the percentage of students with blonde hair between the two groups?

➜

2 Students in two different schools (X and Y) sit the same maths exam. The numbers of students achieving each grade (A to E) are shown in the pie charts below.

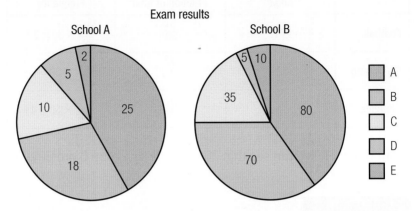

Exam results

School A   School B

□ A
□ B
□ C
□ D
□ E

a) Which school achieved the highest percentage of A grades?
b) Which school achieved the highest percentage of B grades?
c) Write a brief comparison between the results of the two schools.

3 Three companies (X, Y and Z) publish data about the numbers of men and women they employ and their ages. These pie charts show a summary of the data.

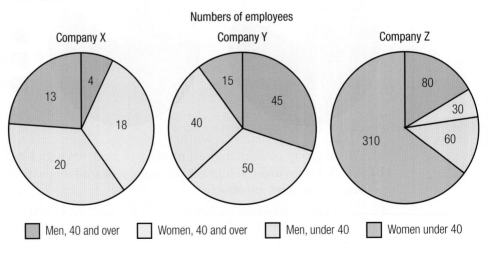

Numbers of employees

Company X   Company Y   Company Z

■ Men, 40 and over   □ Women, 40 and over   □ Men, under 40   ■ Women under 40

Write a short report comparing the percentages of employees in each group in the three companies.

20 Calculations and mental strategies 3

◆ Use the laws of arithmetic and inverse operations to simplify calculations with integers and fractions.
◆ Divide integers and decimals by a single-digit number, continuing the division to a specified number of decimal places, e.g. 68 ÷ 7.
◆ Use the order of operations, including brackets, with more complex calculations.
◆ Recall simple equivalent fractions, decimals and percentages.
◆ Use known facts and place value to calculate simple fractions and percentages of quantities.

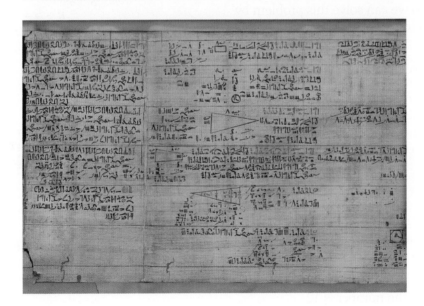

People have been working with fractions for thousands of years.

The introduction to Chapter 9 was about the Rhind papyrus, which was written in Ancient Egypt in about 1650 BCE. The first part of this papyrus is about fractions. It gives an expression for each fraction of the type '2 divided by an odd number from 3 to 101' as a sum of no more than four **unit fractions**.

For example,

$$\frac{2}{15} = \frac{1}{10} + \frac{1}{30} \quad \text{and} \quad \frac{2}{101} = \frac{1}{101} + \frac{1}{202} + \frac{1}{303} + \frac{1}{606}$$

A unit fraction is a fraction in which the numerator is 1.

The papyrus then gives expressions for fractions of the type 'a number divided by 10'. For example,

$$\frac{7}{10} = \frac{2}{3} + \frac{1}{30}$$

Many of the 40 algebraic problems on the papyrus involve fractions too, starting with ways of dividing different numbers of loaves of bread between ten men.

Mental strategies

Inverse operations

You can use the laws of arithmetic and inverse operations to work out problems.

Worked examples

a) If you subtract 5 from a number, the answer is 8. What is the number?
The inverse of subtraction is addition, so we can solve this problem by adding 5 to 8.
$$5 + 8 = 13$$

So the number is 13.

> This can also be solved using algebra:
> $$n - 5 = 8$$
> $$n = 8 + 5$$
> $$n = 13$$

b) A number divided by 7 is 3. What is the number?
The inverse of division is multiplication, so we need to multiply 3 by 7.
$$3 \times 7 = 21$$

So the number is 21.

> Using algebra:
> $$n \div 7 = 3$$
> $$n = 7 \times 3$$
> $$n = 21$$

c) 5 times a number is 60. What is the number?
The inverse of multiplication is division, so we need to divide 60 by 5.
$$60 \div 5 = 12$$

So the number is 12.

> Using algebra:
> $$5n = 60$$
> $$n = 60 \div 5$$
> $$n = 12$$

EXERCISE 20.1A

Solve these problems in your head.

1 8 is added to a number and the total is 20. What is the number?

2 5 is subtracted from a number. The result is 9. What is the number?

3 6 times a number is 54. What is the number?

4   A number divided by 7 is 6. What is the number?

5   The temperature is 17 °C. If it has gone up by 8 °C during the day, what was the starting temperature?

6   One-fifth of a number is 12. What is the number?

7   A number is doubled and then 3 is subtracted. The answer is 15. What is the number?

8   A number is multiplied by 3 and 5 is added. The answer is 26. What is the number?

9   A number is multiplied by itself and 1 is added. The total is 65. What is the number?

10   A number is halved and then 5 is subtracted. The answer is 20. What is the number?

The order of operations

You know that mathematical operations are carried out in a particular order:

- **B**rackets — Any operation in brackets is done first.

- **I**ndices — A number raised to a power (index) is done next.

- **D**ivision and/or **M**ultiplication — Multiplications and divisions are done next. Their order does not matter.

- **A**ddition and/or **S**ubtraction — Additions and subtractions are carried out last. Again, their order is not important.

A way of remembering this order is with the shorthand **BIDMAS**. You need to follow this order when you do calculations in your head, as well as on paper.

Worked examples

a)   Calculate $6 + 5 \times 4 - 3$.

$6 + 5 \times 4 - 3$ *The multiplication is done first ($5 \times 4 = 20$) ...*

$= 6 + 20 - 3$ *... then the addition of 6 and subtraction of 3.*

$= 23$ →

b) Calculate $9 + 7 \times 9 - 18$.

$9 + 7 \times 9 - 18$
The multiplication is done first ($7 \times 9 = 63$) ...

$= 9 + 63 - 18$
... then the addition and subtraction.

$= 72 - 18$

$= 54$

c) Calculate $5 - (8 + 3) \times 6$.

$5 - (8 + 3) \times 6$
The brackets are done first ($8 + 3 = 11$) ...

$= 5 - 11 \times 6$
... then the multiplication by 6 ($11 \times 6 = 66$) ...

$= 5 - 66$
... and finally this is subtracted from 5.

$= -61$

d) Calculate $81 - (10 - 3) - 3(8 + 2)$.

$81 - (10 - 3) - 3(8 + 2)$
The two brackets are done first ...

$= 81 - 7 - 3 \times 10$
... then the multiplication ...

$= 81 - 7 - 30$
... then the addition and subtraction.

$= 81 - 37$

$= 44$

EXERCISE 20.1B

Do these calculations in your head.

1 $4 + 4 \times 2 - 4$

2 $5 \times 2 + 5 \times 3$

3 $5 \times 5 - 5 - 5$

4 $8 + 2 \times 10 - 27$

5 $30 - 2 \times 3 \times 4$

6 $10 \times (3 + 2) - 25$

7 $25 + (12 + 3) \div 3$

8 $24 \div (2 + 6) + 10$

9 $5 + 5 \times 5 - 5$

10 $(8 + 8) \div (12 - 8)$

EXERCISE 20.1C

Copy and complete these calculations, writing in the missing numbers to make them correct.

1 $4 + 4 \times \underline{\hspace{2cm}} - 4 = 12$

2 $5 \times \underline{\hspace{2cm}} + 5 \times 3 = 40$

3 $5 \times 5 - 5 - \underline{\hspace{2cm}} = 10$

4 $10 + \underline{\hspace{2cm}} \times 10 - 30 = 0$

5 $60 - 5 \times \underline{\hspace{2cm}} \times 4 = 0$

6 $\underline{\hspace{2cm}} \times (3 + 7) - 50 = 50$

7 $25 + (\underline{\hspace{2cm}} + 8) \div 4 = 30$

8 $\underline{\hspace{2cm}} \div (6 + 6) + 12 = 14$

9 $8 + 5 \times \underline{\hspace{2cm}} - 8 = 10$

10 $(7 + 6) \div (\underline{\hspace{2cm}} - 9) = 1$

Simplifying calculations

We can use the laws of arithmetic and inverse operations to simplify calculations involving fractions.

Worked examples

a) What is one-fifth of 20?
We can think of this as 20 multiplied by $\frac{1}{5}$ or as 20 divided by $\frac{5}{1}$.
$$20 \div 5 = 4$$

So one-fifth of 20 is 4.

b) Eight bars of chocolate are each divided into quarters. How many pieces are there?
8 divided by $\frac{1}{4}$ is the same as 8 times $\frac{4}{1}$.
$$8 \times 4 = 32$$

So there are 32 pieces.

c) Work out $20 - 8 \div \frac{1}{2}$.
$20 - 8 \div \frac{1}{2}$
$= 20 - 16$
$= 4$

Work out the division first
($8 \div \frac{1}{2} = 8 \times 2$).

d) Work out $(20 - 8) \div \frac{1}{2}$.
$(20 - 8) \div \frac{1}{2}$
$= 12 \div \frac{1}{2}$
$= 12 \times 2$
$= 24$

Work out the bracket first.

EXERCISE 20.1D

Do these calculations in your head.

1 $\frac{1}{5}$ of 35

2 $3 + \frac{1}{4}$ of 28

3 How many ninths in 2?

4 4 divided by $\frac{1}{3}$

5 $7 + 2$ divided by $\frac{1}{2}$

6 $\frac{1}{5}$ of $50 - 10$

7 $\frac{1}{5}(50 - 10)$

8 3 divided by $(1 - \frac{1}{2})$

9 3 divided by $2 - \frac{1}{2}$

10 $\frac{1}{5}$ of $25 - 5$

EXERCISE 20.1E

Do these calculations in your head.

1 **a)** $\frac{1}{5}$ of 45   **b)** $\frac{2}{5}$ of 45   **c)** $\frac{3}{5}$ of 45

2 **a)** $\frac{1}{8}$ of 64   **b)** $\frac{3}{8}$ of 64   **c)** $\frac{7}{8}$ of 64

3 **a)** $\frac{1}{10}$ of 130   **b)** $\frac{5}{10}$ of 130   **c)** $\frac{9}{10}$ of 130

4 **a)** $\frac{1}{8}$ of 160   **b)** $\frac{5}{8}$ of 160   **c)** $\frac{7}{8}$ of 160

5 **a)** $\frac{1}{6}$ of 36   **b)** $\frac{1}{3}$ of 36   **c)** $\frac{5}{6}$ of 36

Percentages

You can use the equivalences between fractions, decimals and percentages to simplify percentage calculations.

Worked examples

a) Find 25% of 240.
We know that 25% is equivalent to $\frac{1}{4}$.
$\frac{1}{4}$ of $240 = 240 \div 4 = 60$
So 25% of 240 is 60.

b) Find 30% of 150.
We know that 30% is equivalent to $\frac{3}{10}$.
$\frac{1}{10}$ of $150 = 15$
$\frac{3}{10}$ of 150 is 3 times as much as $\frac{1}{10}$.
So $\frac{3}{10}$ of $150 = 3 \times 15 = 45$.

EXERCISE 20.1F

Copy and complete this table.

Fraction	Decimal	Percentage
$\frac{1}{2}$		
	0.25	
		75%
$\frac{1}{8}$		
	0.375	
		62.5%
$\frac{7}{8}$		
	0.1	
		20%
$\frac{3}{10}$		
	0.4	
		60%
$\frac{7}{10}$		
	0.8	
		90%

EXERCISE 20.1G

1 Work out these percentages in your head.

a) 50% of 340
b) 75% of 800
c) 40% of 400
d) 25% of 640
e) 80% of 150
f) 37.5% of 320
g) 87.5% of 800
h) 12.5% of 640

2 a) What is 75% of 80?
b) What is 80% of 75?
c) What do you notice about your answers to parts a) and b)?

3 What is 50% of 30 plus 30% of 50?

Written methods

Here are some divisions:

$$72 \div 9 = 8 \quad 56 \div 8 = 7 \quad 45 \div 5 = 9$$

The first number (72, 56 and 45) is called the **dividend**, and the number it is divided by (9, 8 and 5) is called the **divisor**. In the divisions above there is no remainder, but this would not be the case for $73 \div 9$.

$$73 \div 9 = 8 \text{ remainder } 1, \text{ or } 8\tfrac{1}{9}$$

It is more common, though, to continue the division rather than simply writing the remainder. How long to continue the division depends on the calculation or on the number of decimal places asked for in the question.

The examples below are done as long divisions to show the steps clearly.

Worked examples

a) Calculate $22 \div 7$. Give your answer to two decimal places.

```
        3.1 4 2
   7 | 2 2.0 0 0
       2 1
       1 0
         7
       ─────
         3 0
         2 8
       ─────
           2 0
```

Write zeros after the decimal point so that you can continue the division.

Continue the calculation until the third decimal place so that you can round the answer correctly.

Therefore $22 \div 7 = 3.142 = 3.14$
(to two decimal places).

b) Calculate 59 ÷ 8. Give your answer to two decimal places.

```
         7.3 7 5
    8 | 5 9.0 0 0
        5 6
        ‾‾‾
          3 0
          2 4
          ‾‾‾
            6 0
            5 6
            ‾‾‾
              4 0
```

In this example the answer is rounded up.

Therefore 59 ÷ 8 = 7.375 = 7.38
(to two decimal places).

<hr>

EXERCISE 20.2A

Calculate the following by long or short division. Give your answers to two decimal places.

1	47 ÷ 5	**2**	38 ÷ 7
3	46 ÷ 9	**4**	53 ÷ 6
5	50 ÷ 8	**6**	35 ÷ 4
7	142 ÷ 8	**8**	275 ÷ 3
9	456 ÷ 2	**10**	538 ÷ 7

When the number being divided is not a whole number or if you are asked to give your answer to a different degree of accuracy, the procedure is the same.

Worked examples

a) Calculate 42.35 ÷ 7. Give your answer to two decimal places.

```
         6.0 5
    7 | 4 2.3 5
        4 2
        ‾‾‾
          0 3
          0 0
          ‾‾‾
            3 5
            3 5
            ‾‾‾
              0
```

In this example the division ended after two decimal places as there was no remainder.

So 42.35 ÷ 7 to two decimal places is 6.05.

b) Calculate 148.8 ÷ 9. Give your answer to three decimal places.

```
        1 6.5 3 3 3
    9 | 1 4 8.8 0 0 0
        9
        ─────
          5 8
          5 4
          ─────
            4 8
            4 5
            ─────
              3 0
              2 7
              ─────
                3 0
                2 7
                ─────
                  3 0
                  2 7
                  ─────
                    3 0
```

Therefore 148.8 ÷ 9 = 16.533 (to three decimal places).

EXERCISE 20.2B

Calculate the following divisions. Give your answers to two decimal places.

1 27.77 ÷ 2   **2** 19.75 ÷ 3

3 185.78 ÷ 4   **4** 240.55 ÷ 5

5 682.9 ÷ 6   **6** 128.43 ÷ 7

7 289.9 ÷ 8   **8** 146.78 ÷ 9

9 287.3 ÷ 3   **10** 852.74 ÷ 2

EXERCISE 20.2C

Calculate the following divisions. Give your answers to three decimal places.

1 64 ÷ 9   **2** 76 ÷ 6

3 87 ÷ 7   **4** 50 ÷ 3

5 5 ÷ 9   **6** 7 ÷ 6

7 8 ÷ 3   **8** 485 ÷ 8

9 64 ÷ 7   **10** 11 ÷ 3

EXERCISE 20.2D

Give your answers to these questions to two decimal places.

1 Eight cabbages together weigh 6.25 kg. What is the average (mean) weight of one cabbage?

2 The total weight of eight eggs is 340 g. What does each egg weigh?

3 Two identical cars together weigh 2232.5 kg. What does each car weigh?

4 Nine buckets have a total capacity of 76.38 litres. What is the capacity of each bucket?

5 A tanker has eight compartments. The total capacity is 150 000 tonnes. What is the capacity of each compartment?

6 A sea wall is made of 600 concrete sections. The total mass is 10 000 tonnes. What is the mass of each block?

7 A train travels from Sydney to Adelaide and back. The total journey time is 46 hours 18 minutes. How long does each journey take?

8 Divide $105 000 equally between seven people.

9 Seven blocks of chocolate weigh 3320 g. What is the weight of one block?

10 A block of eight identical apartments has a combined volume of 6000 cubic metres. What is the volume of each apartment?

EXERCISE 20.2E

Give your answers to these questions to three decimal places.

1 A 11.5 m length of wood is cut into four equal pieces. How long is each piece?

2 Three identical cars just fit into a trailer which is 18.3 m long. How long is each car?

3 A tower is made from eight identical metal cuboids. The tower is 60.2 m tall. How tall is each of the cuboids?

4 Five identical containers just fit end to end on the deck of a ship. The total length of the deck is 183.4 m. What is the length of each container?

5 A pile of four cans of beans is 46.3 cm tall. How tall is each can?

6 Divide $374.50 equally between seven boys.

7   Nine coaches are parked so that they just touch. The total length is 186.5 m. How long is each coach?

8   A train has six carriages. The total length of the carriages is 210 m. How long is each carriage?

9   Seven identical carpets make a pile 32 cm high. How thick is each carpet?

10 Divide $504 equally between six girls.

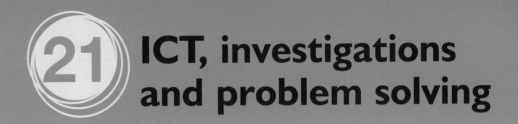

21 ICT, investigations and problem solving

1 Cut corners

Here is a square of side length 10 cm.
Look at how the sides are numbered.

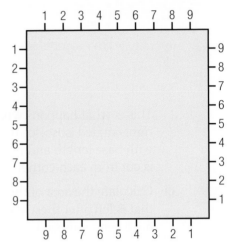

A right-angled isosceles triangle with base length and height 1 cm is cut from each corner.

a) Calculate the area of the shape that is left after the corners have been removed.

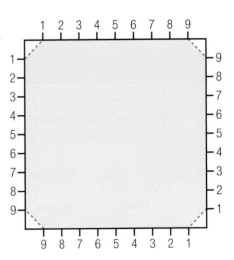

A right-angled isosceles triangle with base length and height 2 cm is cut from each corner.

b) Calculate the area of the shape that is left after these corners have been removed.

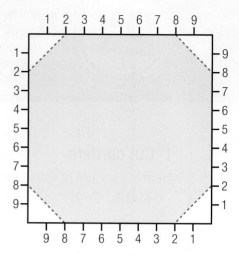

This is what happens when a right-angled isosceles triangle with base length and height 7 cm is cut from each corner.

c) Calculate the area of the shape that is left after these corners have been removed.

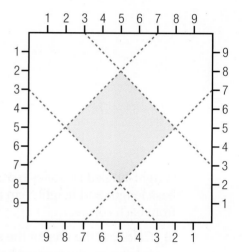

d) Copy and complete this table to find the area of the piece left when different-sized isosceles triangles have been cut from each corner.

Base length and height of triangle	Total area of pieces removed	Area of piece left
0 cm		
1 cm		
2 cm		
3 cm		
4 cm		
5 cm		

Base length and height of triangle	Total area of pieces removed	Area of piece left
6 cm		
7 cm		
8 cm		
9 cm		
10 cm		

e) Can you see a pattern in your results? Write a sentence to explain what happens as you cut triangles from the corner of a square.

f) Write an algebraic rule for the pattern you found in part **e)**.

g) What is the result if other right-angled triangles, which are not isosceles triangles, are cut from the corners of the square?

2 ICT

It is possible to draw a circle passing through the three vertices (corners) of a triangle. Below are instructions showing how to use the geometry package Cabri Géomètre II to demonstrate this.

This investigation can also be done on paper using a ruler and a pair of compasses.

a) Select the 'Triangle' option from the toolbar.

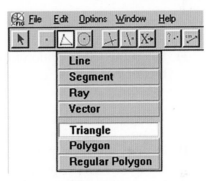

b) Draw a triangle by clicking the mouse at its vertices. (On clicking the third vertex, the shape will automatically close to create a triangle.)

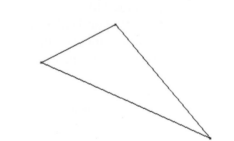

c) To find the circumcentre of the triangle (the centre of the circle passing through the vertices of the triangle), you need to draw the perpendicular bisector of each side of the triangle. To do this, select the 'Perpendicular Bisector' option from the toolbar.

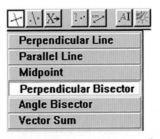

d) Once this has been done, move the mouse over each of the three sides of the triangle in turn. The confirmation 'Perpendicular bisector of this side of the triangle' will appear each time. Clicking the mouse on each of the three sides of the triangle will produce this screen.

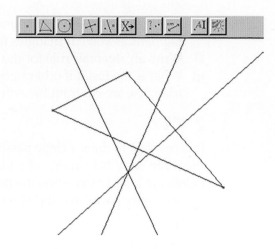

e) Select the 'Circle' option from the toolbar.

f) To draw the circle, place the mouse on the point of intersection of the three perpendicular bisectors and click. (At this point you will be prompted to select two of the three perpendicular bisectors.) Move the mouse out until the circumference passes through one of the vertices of the triangle. Then click the mouse to complete the construction.

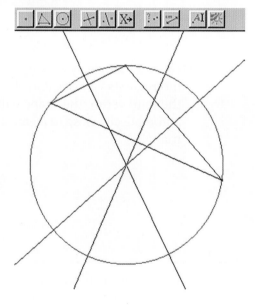

g) To see how the construction changes dynamically, select the 'pointer' tool.

h) Place the pointer tool over one of the vertices of the triangle and 'click and drag'. Describe what you see happening on the screen as you drag the vertex.

Review 3A

1 Convert each of the following to a decimal.

    a) $\frac{13}{20}$ **b)** $\frac{13}{25}$ **c)** $\frac{13}{80}$

2 Convert each of the following to a mixed number.

    a) 3.125   **b)** 1.6   **c)** 2.38

3 A large bag of mixed nuts and raisins states on the label that it contains the following fractions of nuts:

    $\frac{1}{4}$ brazil $\frac{1}{10}$ hazel $\frac{7}{40}$ peanut $\frac{1}{8}$ almond $\frac{3}{25}$ macadamia

    a) Change these fractions to decimals, then write down the nuts in ascending order of their proportion in the mixture.

    b) The rest of the bag is raisins. What percentage of the bag is raisins?

4 A coat priced at $124 is discounted by 25% in a sale. What is the sale price?

5 The first four terms of a sequence are given below.

    9   7   5   3

    a) Describe the term-to-term rule.

    b) Calculate the tenth term.

    c) Write down an expression for the nth term.

6 **a)** Calculate the size of angle a in this diagram. Give reasons for your answer.

    b) Calculate the size of angle b. Give reasons for your answer.

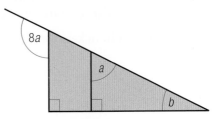

7 The dimensions of a cuboid are as shown.

    a) Write an expression for the surface area of the cuboid in terms of a.

    b) The surface area is 445.5 cm². Calculate the value of a.

    c) Calculate the volume of the cuboid.

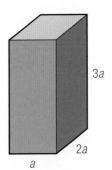

8 Use the formula for the area of a rectangle to work out the missing values in this table.

	Length	Width	Area
a)	7.5 cm	1.2 cm	
b)	12.5 cm		250 cm²
c)		25 cm	175 cm²
d)		15 cm	187.5 cm²

9 The lengths (in centimetres) of some snakes of two different species are given in this table.

Length (cm)	Frequency	
	Species A	Species B
$50 \leqslant L < 60$	15	1
$60 \leqslant L < 70$	12	2
$70 \leqslant L < 80$	2	16
$80 \leqslant L < 90$	1	8
$90 \leqslant L < 100$	0	3

a) What is the modal length of the snakes from each of the species?
b) Another snake is caught and measured. Its length is 78 cm.
　(i) Which of these species is this snake likely to be?
　(ii) Can the snake be from the other species? Explain your answer.

10 Eight tickets for a cup final cost $416. What is the cost of one ticket?

1 An engineer earns \$3200 per month. He pays 25% of his earnings as tax, 30% as rent on his house and puts another 12% into a savings account. Calculate the amount of money he has left for other expenses each month.

2 A car rental company has a fleet of 288 cars. Of these, 36 are being serviced at any one time. What percentage of the fleet is available for hire?

3 For each of the following sequences:
   (i) write down the next two terms
   (ii) write down an expression for the nth term.

   a) 0 3 6 9 12
   b) −1.5 −1 −0.5 0 0.5

4 A straight line is plotted on this coordinate grid.
   a) Write down the coordinates of four points on the line.
   b) From the coordinates deduce the equation of the straight line.

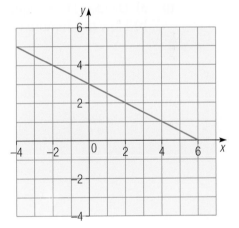

5 Calculate the size of each of the unknown angles in this diagram. Give reasons for your answers.

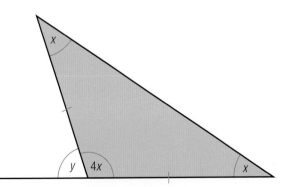

6 This shape was made from a rectangle with dimensions 12 cm × 8 cm.
A semicircle has been removed from each end.
   a) Calculate the area of the coloured region.
   b) Calculate the perimeter of the shape.

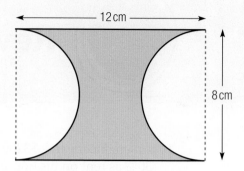

7 a) Explain the difference between the mean, median and mode of a set of data.
   b) Give a disadvantage of each of these averages.
   c) Give an advantage of each of these averages.

8 Nine identical cars are parked in line so that they touch. The total length is 43.38 m. What is the length of one car?

9 a) Calculate 66 ÷ 7. Give your answer to two decimal places.
   b) Multiply your answer to part **a)** by 7. Why is the answer not 66?

10 a) Divide $115.50 equally between seven girls.
   b) How much more would you need in order to give $20 to each girl?

SECTION ④

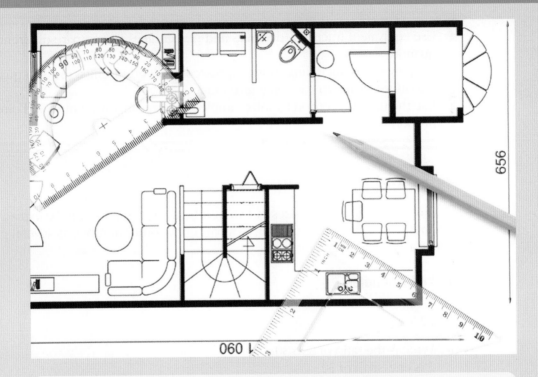

656

060 |

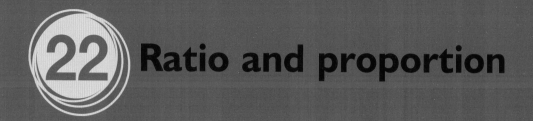

22 Ratio and proportion

◆ Use equivalent fractions, decimals and percentages to compare different quantities.
◆ Simplify ratios, including those expressed in different units; divide a quantity into more than two parts in a given ratio.
◆ Use the unitary method to solve simple problems involving ratio and direct proportion.

Ratio and proportion

A **ratio** shows the relative sizes of two numbers. One number can be expressed as a multiple of the other number, as a part of the other number, as several parts of it or as a percentage of it.

Worked examples

a) What is the ratio of 20 to 4?
20 is 5 times 4.

b) What is the ratio of 5 to 30?
5 is one-sixth of 30.

c) What is the ratio of 25 to 30?
25 is five-sixths of 30.

d) What is the ratio of 5 to 20 as a percentage?
5 is a quarter of 20.
A quarter of 100% is 25%.
So 5 is 25% of 20.

Equivalent ratios

If two ratios are equivalent then they are in **proportion**. For example, the ratios 3 to 6 and 10 to 20 are equivalent (in proportion) because 3 is half of 6 and 10 is half of 20.

Worked examples

a) Are the ratios $8:12$ and $48:72$ equivalent?
8 is two-thirds of 12 and 48 is two-thirds of 72, so the ratios are equivalent.

b) Are the ratios 18 to 12 and 60 to 40 in proportion?
18 is one and a half times 12 and 60 is one and a half times 40, so the ratios are in proportion.

c) Are the ratios 24 to 8 and 12 to 3 in proportion?
24 is 3 times 8 and 12 is 4 times 3, so the ratios are not in proportion.

EXERCISE 22.1A

Which of the following pairs of ratios are in proportion? Give reasons for your answers.

1	1 to 5 and 4 to 20	**2**	2 to 6 and 3 to 9
3	5 to 25 and 15 to 75	**4**	18 to 12 and 40 to 60
5	7 to 21 and 21 to 42	**6**	9 to 18 and 18 to 9
7	5 to 10 and 12 to 24	**8**	6 to 30 and 5 to 20
9	1 to 3 and 3 to 1	**10**	5 to 25 and 20 to 100

Equivalent fractions

A fraction is also a relationship between two numbers, similar to a ratio.
We can use this to see whether two fractions are equivalent. For example, look at these fractions.

$$\frac{1}{4} \qquad \frac{5}{20}$$

The ratio of 1 to 4 is the same as 5 to 20, so the fractions are equivalent.

Worked examples

a) Complete this pair of equivalent fractions.

$$\frac{5}{2} = \frac{20}{\square}$$

We need to find the number that is in the same ratio to 20 as 2 is to 5.

Five is two and a half times 2 and 20 is two and a half times 8.

So 5 to 2 is equivalent to 20 to 8.

$$\frac{5}{2} = \frac{20}{8}$$

b) Complete this pair of equivalent fractions.

$$\frac{3}{5} = \frac{12}{\boxed{}}$$

The ratio of 3 to 5 is the same as the ratio of 12 to 20, since $12 = 3 \times 4$ and $20 = 5 \times 4$.

$$\frac{3}{5} = \frac{12}{20}$$

There are other ways of getting 'the answer' but it is important to think in terms of ratios.

EXERCISE 22.1B

Copy these pairs of equivalent fractions and fill in the missing numbers.

1 $\dfrac{3}{2}$ and $\dfrac{6}{\boxed{}}$

2 $\dfrac{8}{9}$ and $\dfrac{24}{\boxed{}}$

3 $\dfrac{7}{8}$ and $\dfrac{\boxed{}}{16}$

4 $\dfrac{4}{5}$ and $\dfrac{\boxed{}}{50}$

5 $\dfrac{3}{4}$ and $\dfrac{9}{\boxed{}}$

6 $\dfrac{18}{24}$ and $\dfrac{3}{\boxed{}}$

7 $\dfrac{8}{12}$ and $\dfrac{12}{\boxed{}}$

8 $\dfrac{1}{9}$ and $\dfrac{9}{\boxed{}}$

9 $\dfrac{4}{10}$ and $\dfrac{40}{\boxed{}}$

10 $\dfrac{16}{36}$ and $\dfrac{24}{\boxed{}}$

Percentages

A percentage is another way of expressing a relationship between two numbers.

It is the ratio of a number to 100. For example, 20% is the same as the ratio of 20 to 100 (or one-fifth) and 300% is the same as the ratio of 300 to 100 (or 3 times).

So 20% of 30 is the same as one-fifth of 30 (or 6) and 300% of 6 is the same as $3 \times 6 = 18$.

The table shows the percentage equivalents of some ratios written in words.

Ratio	Percentage
a half	50%
a quarter	25%
three quarters	75%
twice as much	200%
ten times as big	1000%

Worked example

Express $\frac{2}{5}$ as a percentage.

$$\frac{2}{5} = \frac{\square}{100}$$

$\frac{2}{5}$ is equivalent to $\frac{40}{100}$, since $100 = 20 \times 5$

and $40 = 20 \times 2$.

So $\frac{2}{5}$ as a percentage is 40%.

> We need to find the number that is in the same ratio to 100 as 2 is to 5.

EXERCISE 22.1C

Copy and complete these sets of equivalent fractions and percentages.

1 $\dfrac{8}{24} = \dfrac{1}{\square}$

2 $\dfrac{5}{9} = \dfrac{\square}{18}$

3 $\dfrac{7}{10} = \square\%$

4 $\dfrac{11}{100} = \square\%$

5 $\dfrac{13}{50} = \square\%$

6 $\dfrac{17}{51} = \dfrac{1}{\square}$

7 $\dfrac{8}{25} = \dfrac{\square}{50} = \square\%$

8 $\dfrac{10}{125} = \dfrac{\square}{1000} = \square\%$

9 $\dfrac{7}{50} = \dfrac{\square}{100} = \square\%$

10 $\dfrac{35}{1000} = \dfrac{\square}{200} = \square\%$

Writing a percentage as a decimal is relatively straightforward.

Worked examples

a)   Write 20% as a decimal.

    $20\% = \frac{20}{100} = 0.2$

b)   Write 16% as a decimal.

    $16\% = \frac{16}{100} = 0.16$

c)   Write 7% as a decimal.

    $7\% = \frac{7}{100} = 0.07$

So we can write a relationship between numbers as a ratio, a fraction, a decimal and a percentage. For example, one-fifth and 0.2 and 20% are all equivalent. They are in proportion.

$$\frac{1}{5} = \frac{20}{100} \quad \text{and} \quad 0.2 = \frac{20}{100} \quad \text{and} \quad 20\% = \frac{20}{100}$$

EXERCISE 22.1D

Which of the following are equivalent (in proportion)? Give reasons for your answers.

1 $\frac{1}{10}$ 0.1   10%   **2** $\frac{1}{5}$ 0.5   50%

3 $\frac{1}{8}$ 0.125   12.5%   **4** $\frac{1}{3}$ 0.3   3%

5 $\frac{4}{5}$ 0.8   8%   **6** $\frac{3}{8}$ 0.375   37.5%

7 $\frac{2}{3}$ 0.6   60%   **8** $\frac{9}{100}$ 0.9   9%

9 $\frac{1}{20}$ 0.05   5%   **10** 2   2.0   200%

EXERCISE 22.1E

Copy and complete this table.

Fraction	Ratio	Percentage
$\frac{1}{2}$	1 to 2	50%
$\frac{1}{4}$	1 to ☐	25%
$\frac{3}{4}$	☐ to 4	
$\frac{1}{8}$	1 to ☐	12.5%
$\frac{3}{8}$	☐ to 8	
$\frac{5}{8}$	5 to ☐	
$\frac{7}{8}$		87.5%
$\frac{1}{10}$	1 to ☐	10%
$\frac{2}{10}$ or $\frac{1}{5}$	☐ to 5	20%
$\frac{3}{10}$	3 to ☐	
$\frac{4}{10}$ or $\frac{2}{5}$	☐ to 5	
$\frac{6}{10}$ or $\frac{3}{5}$	☐ to 5	
$\frac{7}{10}$		70%
$\frac{8}{10}$ or $\frac{4}{5}$		
$\frac{9}{10}$	9 to 10	

Simplifying ratios

Like fractions, ratios can be simplified. For example,

4:8 simplifies to 1:2, as 4 = 4 × 1 and 8 = 4 × 2.
14:21 simplifies to 2:3, as 14 = 7 × 3 and 21 = 7 × 3.

Worked example

Simplify the ratio 2 litres : 750 m*l*.

2 litres = 2000 m*l*

2000 m*l* : 750 m*l* simplifies to 8 : 3,
since 2000 = 250 × 8 and 750 = 250 × 3.

First write both quantities in the same units.

EXERCISE 22.1F

Simplify these ratios.

1	27:36	**2**	45:75
3	28:70	**4**	20 minutes : 1 hour
5	3 kg : 750 g	**6**	8 m : 75 cm
7	7 litres to 750 ml	**8**	$2 to 20 cents
9	3 hours to 1 day	**10**	8 weeks to 1 year

Direct proportion

Workers building houses may be paid for the number of hours they work. Their pay is in **direct proportion** to the hours they work – more hours, more pay.

Workers laying bricks may be paid for the number of bricks they lay, not for the time they work. Their pay is in direct proportion to the number of bricks they lay.

Worked example

A machine for making cups makes 500 cups in 20 minutes.
How many cups does it make in 3 hours?

In 20 minutes 500 cups are made.

So in 1 minute 500 ÷ 20 = 25 cups are made.

3 hours is 180 minutes.

In 3 hours 25 × 180 = 4500 cups are made.

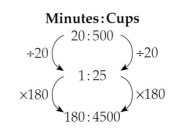

Minutes : Cups
20 : 500
÷20   ÷20
1 : 25
×180   ×180
180 : 4500

The method used in the example on page 215 is called the **unitary method**. In it, you work out the ratio in the form $1:n$ and you multiply by the appropriate value.

the example on page 215

EXERCISE 22.2A

Use the unitary method to solve these problems.

1   A heater uses 3 units of electricity in 40 minutes.
    How many units does it use in 2 hours?

2   A machine prints 1500 newspapers in 45 minutes.
    How many does it print in 12 hours?

3   A bricklayer lays 1200 bricks in an average 8-hour day.
    How many bricks does he lay in a 40-hour week?

4   A combine harvester produces 9 tonnes of grain in 6 hours.
    How many tonnes does it produce in 54 hours?

5   A machine puts tar on a road at the rate of 4 metres in 5 minutes.
    a) How long does it take to cover 1 km of road?
    b) How many metres of road does it cover in 8 hours?

When the information is given as a ratio, the method of solving the problem is the same.

Worked example

Copper and nickel are mixed in the ratio $7:4$.

36 g of nickel are used. How much copper is used?

4 g of nickel is mixed with 7 g of copper.

So 1 g of nickel is mixed with $7 \div 4 = \frac{7}{4}$ g of copper

and 36 g of nickel is mixed with $\frac{7}{4} \times 36 = 7 \times 9 = 63$ g of copper.

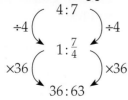

EXERCISE 22.2B

Use the unitary method to solve these problems.

1   The ratio of girls to boys in a class is 6:5.
    There are 18 girls. How many boys are there?

2   Sand and gravel are mixed in the ratio 4:3 to make ballast.
    80 kg of sand is used. How much gravel is used?

3   A paint mix uses blue and white in the ratio 3:10.
    6.6 litres of blue paint are used. How much white paint is used?

4   A necklace has green and blue beads in the ratio 2:3.
    There are 24 green beads on the necklace. How many blue beads are there?

Dividing a quantity in a given ratio

We can also use the unitary method to divide a quantity in a given ratio.

Worked example

A piece of wood is 150 cm long. It is divided into two pieces in the ratio 7:3.

How long is each piece?

A ratio of 7:3 means that you need to consider the wood as 10 parts. One piece of wood is made of 7 parts; the other piece is made of 3 parts.

10 parts are 150 cm long.

So 1 part is 150 cm ÷ 10 = 15 cm long.

7 parts are 7 × 15 cm = 105 cm long

and 3 parts are 3 × 15 cm = 45 cm long.

EXERCISE 22.3

1   Divide 250 in the ratio 3:2.

2   Divide 144 in the ratio 1:2.

3   Divide 10 kg in the ratio 2:3.

4   Divide 1 hour in the ratio 5:7.

5   Divide 8 m in the ratio 3:13.

6   Divide 45 km in the ratio 7:8.

7   Divide 4 hours in the ratio 5:3.

8   Divide 2 kg in the ratio 3:7.

9   Divide 3 litres in the ratio 7:5.

10 Divide 1 m in the ratio 2:3:5.

11 Divide 70 litres in the ratio 1:2:4.

12 Divide 1 hour in the ratio 5:6:9.

13 Divide 2 km in the ratio 3:8:9.

14 Divide 9 kg in the ratio 3:14:19.

15 Divide $75 in the ratio 3:5:7.

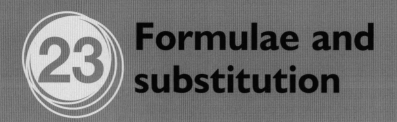

Formulae and substitution

◆ Derive and use simple formulae, e.g. to convert degrees Celsius (°C) to degrees Fahrenheit (°F).

◆ Substitute positive and negative integers into formulae, linear expressions and expressions involving small powers, e.g. $3x^2 + 4$ or $2x^3$, including examples that lead to an equation to solve.

Thermometers measure how 'hot' something is, usually in units called degrees. Three temperature scales are in common use today – the Celsius (°C), Fahrenheit (°F) and Kelvin (K) scales – and they are all different. This is because the inventors of different types of thermometers all chose their own scales.

In the 16th century Galileo invented a thermometer in which air in a glass bulb expanded or contracted, causing water to move in a tube. In 1724 Daniel Fahrenheit invented one using mercury, a metallic liquid which expands readily. His scale went from zero at the coldest temperature he could get to 100 degrees at normal body temperature. In 1742 Anders Celsius proposed a scale with zero at the boiling point of water and 100 at the melting point of ice. (Yes, that is correct – the other way round from the Celsius scale we use today!)

The Fahrenheit scale is still used in the USA and some other countries but the Celsius scale is more widely used. The Fahrenheit and Celsius scales are different: the boiling point of water is at 100 °C and 212 °F and the freezing point of water is at 0 °C and 32 °F. So these two points are 100 degrees Celsius but 212 − 32 = 180 degrees Fahrenheit apart. Later in this chapter you will learn how to convert between these two scales.

People sometimes talk about 'degrees Centigrade' but this is incorrect.

The Kelvin scale is named after Lord Kelvin, an Irish physicist, who wrote of the need for an 'absolute scale' in the 19th century. The size of a degree Kelvin is the same as a degree Celsius but zero K corresponds to about −273 °C. This extremely low temperature is called 'absolute zero'. It is the temperature at which all motion stops and it cannot ever be reached. The Kelvin scale is the scale used internationally in science.

Substitution into an expression

You already know that $a + b$ is an **expression**. If you are told that $a = 3$ and $b = 2$, then you can **substitute** 3 for a and 2 for b into the expression to give $3 + 2$. So the value of the expression $a + b$ when $a = 3$ and $b = 2$ is 5.

When $a = 4$ and $b = 5$, the value of $a + b =$ is 9.

Worked examples

Calculate the value of the expressions below when $a = 3$, $b = 4$, $c = 2$ and $d = -1$.

a) $a + 2b - c + d$
$= 3 + (2 \times 4) - 2 + (-1)$
$= 3 + 8 - 2 - 1$
$= 8$

b) $a^2 - c^3$
$= 3^2 - 2^3$
$= 9 - 8$
$= 1$

c) $3(b - d)^2$
$= 3(4 - (-1))^2$
$= 3 \times 5^2$
$= 3 \times 25$
$= 75$

EXERCISE 23.1

For questions 1–25, calculate the value of the expression when:
a) $a = 5$, $b = 4$, $c = 3$ and $d = 2$
b) $a = -5$, $b = -4$, $c = -3$ and $d = -2$.

1 $a + b$

2 $a - b$

3 $a + b - c$

4 $a + b - c - d$

5 $3a$

6 $4b$

7 $6c$

8 $3d$

9 $3a + 4b + 6c + 3d$

10 $3a - 4b + 6c - 3d$

11 $8a - 4b - 6c - 5d$

12 $a - b - c - d$

13 $2a - 3b - 4c - 5d$

14 a^2

15 b^2

16 c^2

17 d^2

18 $a^2 + b^2$

19 $a^2 - b^2$

20 $a^2 - b^2 + c^2 - d^2$

21 a^3

22 $b^3 - b^2$

23 $c^3 - c^2$

24 $d^3 - 2a$

25 $d^3 - c^3$

Substitution into a formula

You know from Chapter 2 that a **formula** describes the relationship between different variables. You can substitute known values into a formula to find an unknown value.

For example, Newton's second law of motion is that the force on an object is equal to its mass times its acceleration. We can write this relationship as a formula:

$F = ma$

F stands for the force,

m stands for the mass of an object,

a stands for the acceleration.

If we know the mass of an object and its acceleration, we can substitute the values into the formula to find the force. Ignoring the units, if $m = 10$ and $a = 3$ for example,

$F = 10 \times 3 = 30$

Another equation of motion is that the final velocity of an accelerating object is equal to its starting velocity plus acceleration times time.

We can write this relationship as a formula:

$v = u + at$

Velocity is speed in a given direction.

v stands for the final velocity,

u stands for the starting velocity,

a stands for the acceleration,

t stands for the time.

If $u = 20$, $a = 5$ and $t = 10$, we can substitute into the formula to find the final velocity:

$v = 20 + 5 \times 10$

$v = 20 + 50$

$v = 70$

EXERCISE 23.2

1 Given the formula $v = u + at$, find the value of v when:
   a) $u = 8$, $a = 6$ and $t = 10$
   b) $u = 12$, $a = 4$ and $t = 8$
   c) $u = 10$, $a = 10$ and $t = 10$
   d) $u = 25$, $a = -2$ and $t = 8$
   e) $u = 0$, $a = 6$ and $t = 30$

2 Given the formula $s = ut + \frac{1}{2}at^2$, where

   s = displacement (distance from a given point)
   u = starting velocity
   a = acceleration
   t = time

   find the value of s when:
   a) $u = 5$, $t = 10$ and $a = 4$
   b) $u = 0$, $t = 5$ and $a = 2$
   c) $u = 10$, $t = 2$ and $a = 6$
   d) $u = 8$, $t = 5$ and $a = 10$
   e) $u = 0$ and $a = 0$

Converting between temperature scales

You read on page 218 that between the freezing point and the boiling point of water there are 100 degrees on the Celsius scale and 180 degrees on the Fahrenheit scale.

So 100 Celsius units are equivalent to 180 Fahrenheit units.

So 1 Celsius unit is equivalent to 1.8 or $\frac{9}{5}$ Fahrenheit units.

But as the freezing point of water is 32 °F, we will need to add 32 as well.

So temperature in $°F = \frac{9}{5} \times$ temperature in $°C + 32$

that is, $F = \frac{9}{5} C + 32$

Rearranging this gives:

temperature in $°C =$ (temperature in $°F - 32) \times \frac{5}{9}$

that is, $C = \frac{5}{9} (F - 32)$

Worked examples

a) Convert 20 °C to degrees Fahrenheit.

$F = \frac{9}{5} C + 32$

$F = \frac{9}{5} \times 20 + 32$

$F = 36 + 32$

$F = 68$

So 20 °C is equivalent to 68 °F.

b) Convert 104 °F to degrees Celsius.

$C = \frac{5}{9} (F - 32)$

$C = \frac{5}{9} (104 - 32)$

$C = \frac{5}{9} \times 72$

$C = 40$

So 104 °F is equivalent to 40 °C.

EXERCISE 23.3A

Convert these temperatures to degrees Fahrenheit.

1	25 °C	**2**	30 °C
3	−10 °C	**4**	12.5 °C
5	17.5 °C	**6**	100 °C
7	−80 °C	**8**	1000 °C
9	0 °C	**10**	−100 °C

Convert these temperatures to degrees Celsius.

1	32 °F	**2**	68 °F
3	95 °F	**4**	104 °F
5	14 °F	**6**	−4 °F
7	392 °F	**8**	932 °F
9	−148 °F	**10**	302 °F

Useful approximations

A good approximation for converting from degrees Celsius to degrees Fahrenheit is to multiply by 2 and add 30, that is:

$$F \approx 2C + 30$$

Convert each of the temperatures in Exercise 23.3A into degrees Fahrenheit using the approximation above. When is it close and when is it not so good an estimate?

A good approximation for converting from degrees Fahrenheit to degrees Celsius is to subtract 30 and then halve your answer, that is:

$$C \approx \tfrac{1}{2} (F - 30)$$

Convert each of the temperatures in Exercise 23.3B into degrees Celsius using the approximation above. When is it close and when is it not so good an estimate?

Using substitution to form and solve an equation

Sometimes the unknown value is not on its own on the left-hand side of a formula. In these cases, when you substitute the known values into the formula you will be left with an **equation**. You can then solve the equation to find the unknown value.

Worked example

Use the formula $v = u + at$ to find the value of u when $v = 25$, $a = 3$ and $t = 5$.

$$v = u + at$$
$$25 = u + (3 \times 5)$$
$$25 = u + 15$$
$$25 - 15 = u$$
$$u = 10$$

This is an equation.

EXERCISE 23.4

In each of these questions, the values of three of v, u, a and t are given.
Use the formula $v = u + at$ to form an equation and find the missing value.

1 $v = 36$, $a = 4$ and $t = 6$

2 $v = 49$, $a = 5$ and $t = 6$

3 $v = 100$, $a = 8$ and $t = 10$

4 $v = 50$, $a = 5$ and $t = 8$

5 $v = 100$, $a = 9$ and $t = 3$

6 $v = 35$, $a = 3$ and $u = 20$

7 $v = 96$, $a = 8$ and $u = 40$

8 $v = 70$, $a = 6$ and $u = 22$

9 $v = 36$, $t = 3$ and $u = 12$

10 $v = 100$, $t = 15$ and $u = 10$

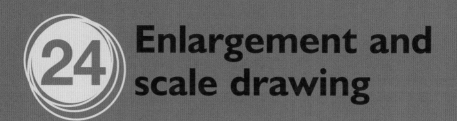

24 Enlargement and scale drawing

◆ Understand and use the language and notation associated with enlargement; enlarge two-dimensional shapes, given a centre of enlargement and a positive integer scale factor.
◆ Interpret and make simple scale drawings.

Enlargement

In Chapter 11 you studied reflection, rotation and translation symmetry, all of which are types of transformation. In each of these cases the final image is the same size as the original object. All that changed was the position and orientation of the object.

Another type of transformation is **enlargement**. With enlargement, the final image usually has a different position and size to the original object.

However, simply stating that the size changes is misleading. In the examples below, picture A is the original object. Picture B shows the object stretched horizontally and picture C shows it stretched vertically.

These stretches are *not* considered to be enlargements. For an object to be enlarged, its lengths must all be multiplied by the same amount.

For example, here, both the horizontal and vertical lengths have been multiplied by 2. We say that the object has been enlarged by a **scale factor** of 2.

In an enlargement, the number which multiplies the lengths is called the **scale factor of enlargement**.

Worked example

Triangle Y is an enlargement of triangle X. Calculate the scale factor of enlargement.

Each of the lengths of triangle Y is three times that of triangle X. Therefore the scale factor of enlargement is 3.

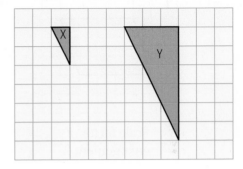

EXERCISE 24.1A

In each of the diagrams below, shape B is bigger than shape A.
a) Decide whether B is an enlargement of A.
b) If B is an enlargement of A, calculate the scale factor of enlargement.

1

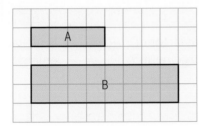

2

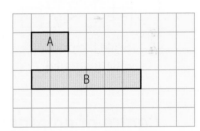

3

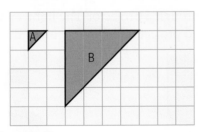

4

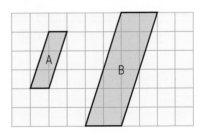

5

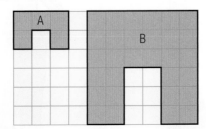

6

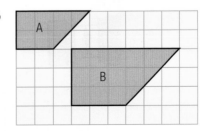

EXERCISE 24.1B

Copy each of the diagrams below on to squared paper and enlarge each of the objects by the given scale factor of enlargement.

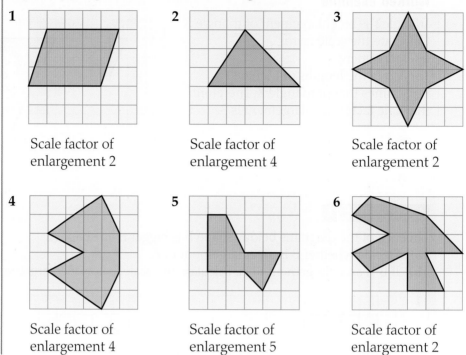

1
Scale factor of enlargement 2

2
Scale factor of enlargement 4

3
Scale factor of enlargement 2

4
Scale factor of enlargement 4

5
Scale factor of enlargement 5

6
Scale factor of enlargement 2

Centre of enlargement

In a cinema, celluloid film passed through a projector. The light source in the projector shone through the film and projected the image on to the screen.

What appears on the screen is an enlargement of what is on the film. In cinemas, the scale factor of enlargement can be over 100. You can model this by using a torch and a shape made from a cut-out piece of cardboard. The light from the torch casts a shadow (image) of the cardboard shape on to a wall or screen.

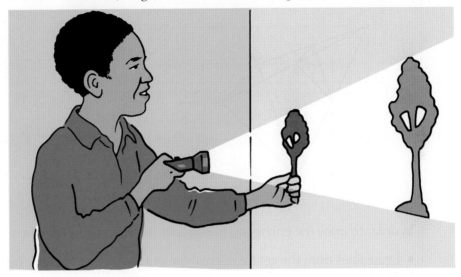

The size and position of the image on the screen depend on the position of the torch in relation to the object. These diagrams demonstrate this.

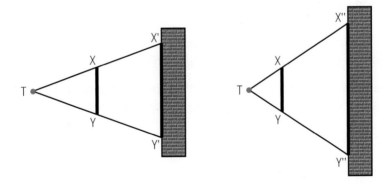

T is the position of the torch.
XY is the length of the object.
$X'Y'$ is the length of the image projected on to the wall.
$X''Y''$ is the length of the image when T is moved closer to the object.

The mathematical way to describe an enlargement is to give both the scale factor of enlargement and the position of the centre of enlargement.

Worked examples

a) Enlarge the triangle *ABC* by a scale factor of 2 and from the centre of enlargement *O* shown.

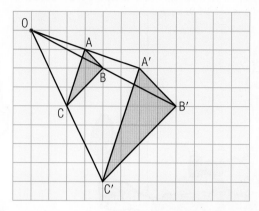

In order to draw the enlargement correctly the following steps were taken.

- Draw lines from the centre of enlargement *O* through each of the vertices *A, B* and *C*.
- As the scale factor of enlargement is 2, draw each of the lines such that *OA'* is twice the length of *OA*, *OB'* is twice the length of *OB* and *OC'* is twice the length of *OC*.
- The ends of each of the lines *OA'*, *OB'* and *OC'* are joined to form the enlarged shape *A'B'C'*.

An easy way of making sure the lines are drawn correctly is to count squares. For example, as OA is 3 across and 1 down, OA' is 6 across and 2 down.

b) This diagram shows a rectangle *ABCD* and its enlargement *A'B'C'D'* from the centre of enlargement *O*. Calculate the scale factor of enlargement.

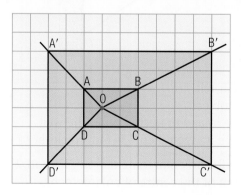

AB = 3 units and *A'B'* = 9 units, so the scale factor of enlargement is 9 ÷ 3 = 3.
To check: *A'D'* = 3 × *AD*.

EXERCISE 24.2A

Copy each of the diagrams below on to squared paper and enlarge each of the objects by the given scale factor of enlargement and from the centre of enlargement O.

A grid larger than the one shown may be needed in some questions.

1

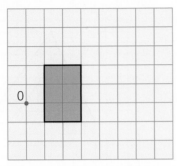

Scale factor of enlargement 2

2

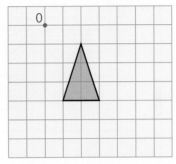

Scale factor of enlargement 2

3

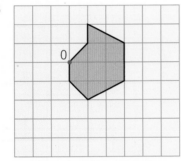

Scale factor of enlargement 2

4

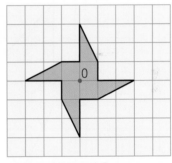

Scale factor of enlargement 3

5

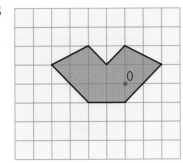

Scale factor of enlargement 3

★ 6

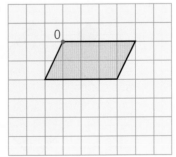

Scale factor of enlargement $1\frac{1}{2}$

EXERCISE 24.2B

In each of the following diagrams, the larger shape is an enlargement of the smaller one from the centre of enlargement *O*. Calculate the scale factor of enlargement in each case.

1

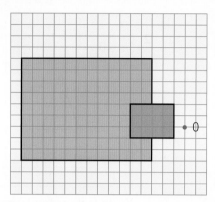

2

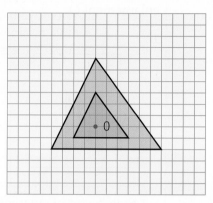

3

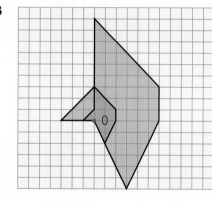

4

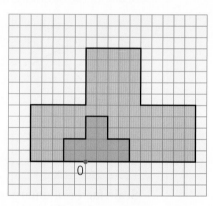

5

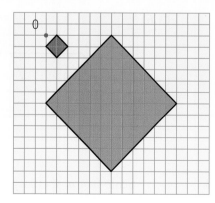

6

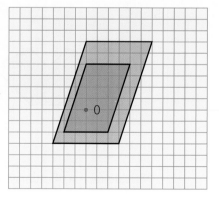

Scale drawings

Sometimes drawing an object to its actual size is not practical or possible. When architects design buildings, for example, they do not produce a life-size drawing of the building. A scale drawing is produced instead. In a scale drawing, all the lengths are changed by the same scale factor.

The scale is shown using a ratio. For example, a scale of $1:50$ means that 1 unit of length on the diagram represents a length which is 50 times bigger on the actual object. Therefore 1 cm on the diagram represents 50 cm in real life.

Worked examples

a) A diagram is drawn to a scale of $1:25$. A line on the diagram has length 20 cm. What actual length does it represent?

$1:25$ means that the actual lengths are 25 times bigger than those drawn.

$20 \times 25 = 500$

So 20 cm on the diagram represents 500 cm (5 m) in real life.

b) This sketch shows the dimensions of a room. Draw a scale diagram of the room with a scale of $1:150$.

$1:150$ means that the lengths on the diagram must be 150 times smaller than those of the actual room. We need to divide by 150.

9 m = 900 cm so the diagram length is 900 cm ÷ 150 = 6 cm.
6 m = 600 cm so the diagram length is 600 cm ÷ 150 = 4 cm.

The scale drawing is as shown.

It is easier to convert the dimensions to centimetres first.

c) A circular arena is being built. On a scale drawing, the radius of the arena is 8 cm. The radius of the actual arena is 120 m. Calculate the scale of the drawing.

To calculate the scale factor of enlargement from the diagram to the actual arena, both lengths must be in the same units.

On the diagram, radius = 8 cm.
In real life, radius = 120 m = 12 000 cm.
Scale factor of enlargement = 12 000 ÷ 8 = 1500

Therefore the scale of the drawing is $1:1500$.

d) A landscape artist makes a scale drawing of a public garden. The scale used is 1 cm represents 10 m.

  (i) The width of the garden on the scale drawing is 18.2 cm. Calculate its real width.

  (ii) The length of the actual garden is 425 m. Calculate its length on the scale drawing.

  (i) 1 cm represents 10 m, so 18.2 cm represents $18.2 \times 10 = 182$ m. The real width is 182 m.

  (ii) 10 m is represented by 1 cm, so 425 m is represented by $425 \div 10 = 42.5$ cm. The length on the drawing is 42.5 cm.

EXERCISE 24.3

1 Calculate the actual length (in metres) represented by each of these lengths on a scale drawing. The scale of each diagram is given in brackets.

  a) 10 cm   (1:50)
  b) 35 cm   (1:30)
  c) 40 mm   (1:100)
  d) 160 mm   (1:150)
  e) 70 cm   (2:75)

2 Calculate the length (in centimetres) that represents each of these actual lengths on a scale drawing. The scale of each diagram is given in brackets.

  a) 60 m   (1:150)
  b) 120 m   (1:2000)
  c) 380 cm   (1:25)
  d) 4 km   (1:5000)
  e) 15 m   (2:75)

3 In each of these pairs of lengths, the first is the length on a scale drawing and the second is the corresponding length in real life. Calculate the scale in each case.

  a) 20 cm   1200 cm
  b) 25 cm   100 m
  c) 5 cm   75 m
  d) 6 cm   0.3 km
  e) 12 mm   600 m

4 Each of these sketches shows the plan view of a room and its actual dimensions.
   (i) Draw a scale diagram of each room using the scale suggested.
   (ii) Write the dimensions (in centimetres) on each diagram.

a)

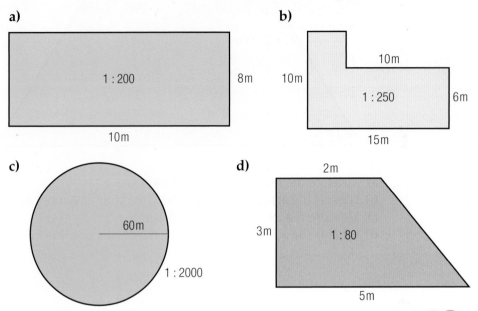

b)

c)

d)

5 Draw a scale diagram of your classroom.

You will need a tape measure, pencil and squared paper.

6 The ground floor of a building is drawn to scale. 1 cm on the drawing represents 10 m in real life.
   a) The length is 8.3 cm on the scale drawing. Calculate the length of the real building.
   b) The width of the actual building is 128 m. Calculate its width on the drawing.

7 This diagram shows the plan of a room drawn to a scale of 1:50.
   a) Measure the length AF in centimetres.
   b) Calculate the actual length AF in the room.
   c) Measure the length CD in centimetres.
   d) Calculate the actual length CD in the room.
   e) Measure the length CF in centimetres.
   f) Calculate the actual length CF in the room.

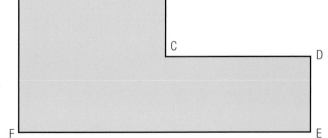

8   This diagram shows the plan of a piece of ground being sold for development. The scale used is 1:2500.

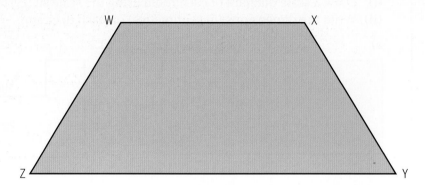

a) Measure the length *WX* in centimetres.
b) What is the actual length of *WX*? Give your answer in metres.
c) Measure the length *WY* in centimetres.
d) What is the actual length of *WY*? Give your answers in metres.

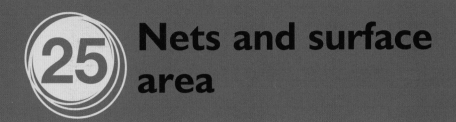

25 Nets and surface area

◆ Draw simple nets of solids, e.g. cuboid, regular tetrahedron, square-based pyramid, triangular prism.
◆ Use simple nets of solids to work out their surface areas.

Nets

A **net** is a two-dimensional representation of the faces of a three-dimensional object. By folding the net up, the three-dimensional object is created.

Package designers need a knowledge and understanding of nets because most types of packaging start off as a net.

Below is the common net of a cube, which you are already familiar with.

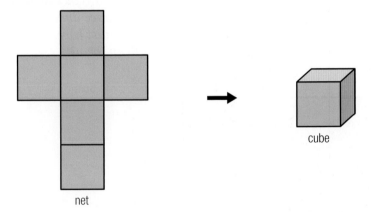

net

cube

There are, however, other nets which will produce a cube. Here are two examples.

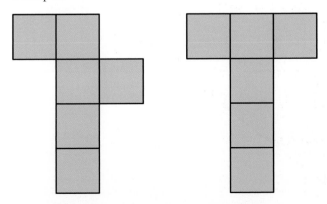

Worked example

Draw two possible nets of this triangular prism.

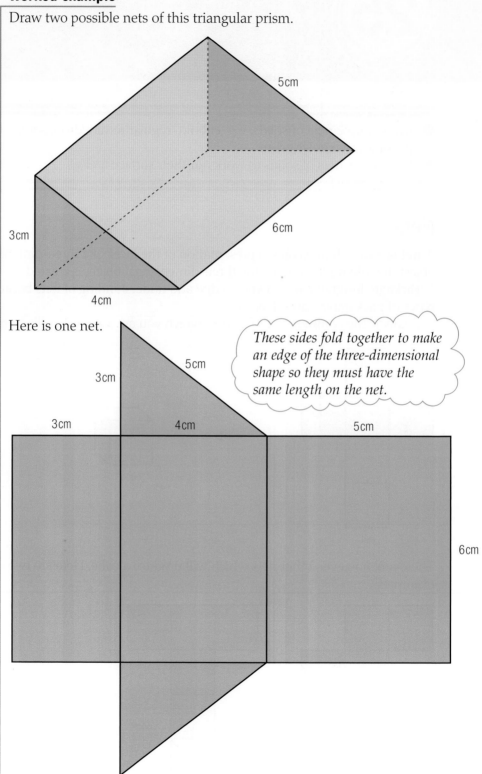

Here is one net.

These sides fold together to make an edge of the three-dimensional shape so they must have the same length on the net.

Another net that will fold to give the same triangular prism is shown here.

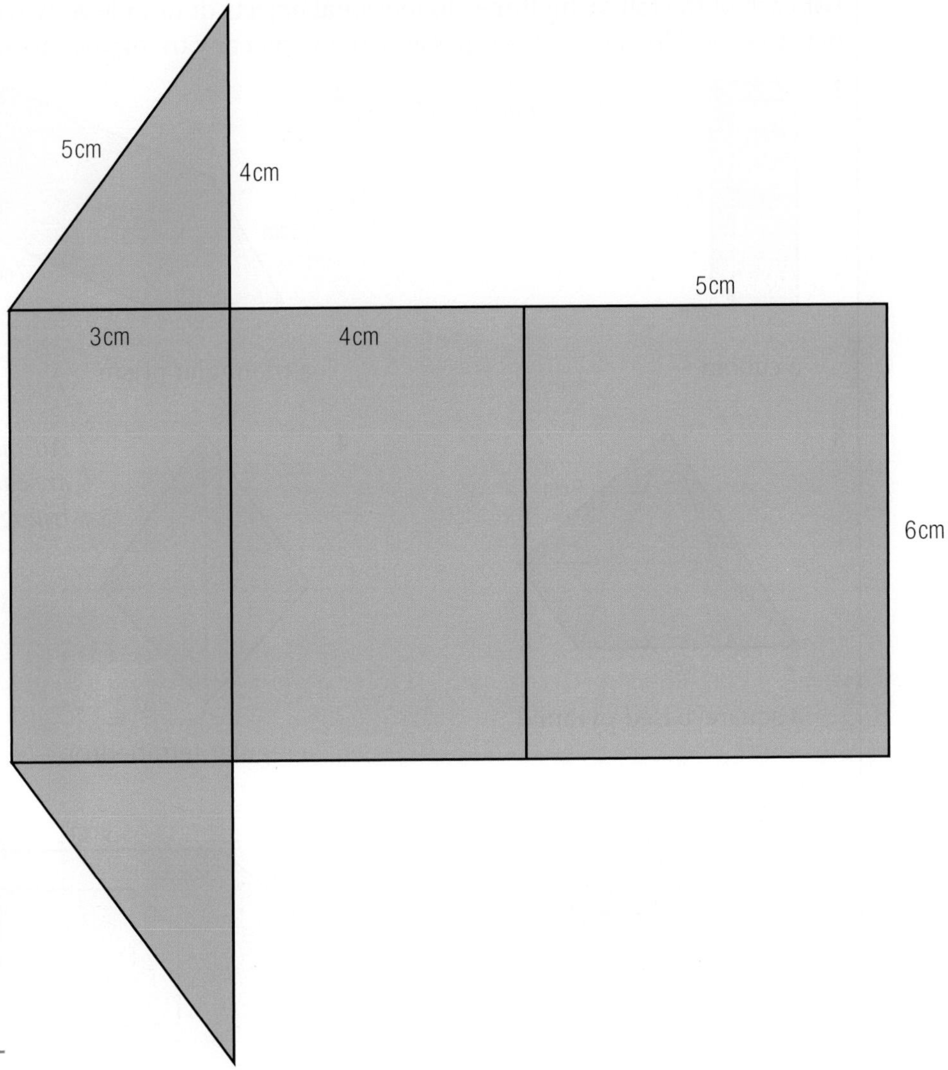

5cm

4cm

3cm

4cm

5cm

6cm

EXERCISE 25.1

For each of the following three-dimensional objects draw at least two different nets to scale. Use a pair of compasses to construct any triangular faces.

1

The name of each shape is given.

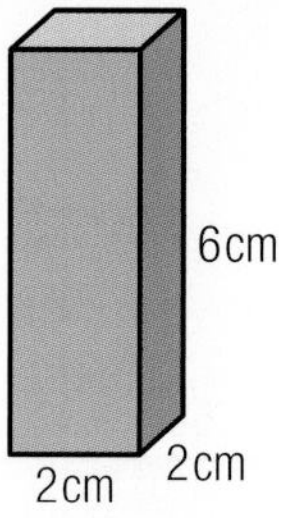

6cm

2cm 2cm

a cuboid

2

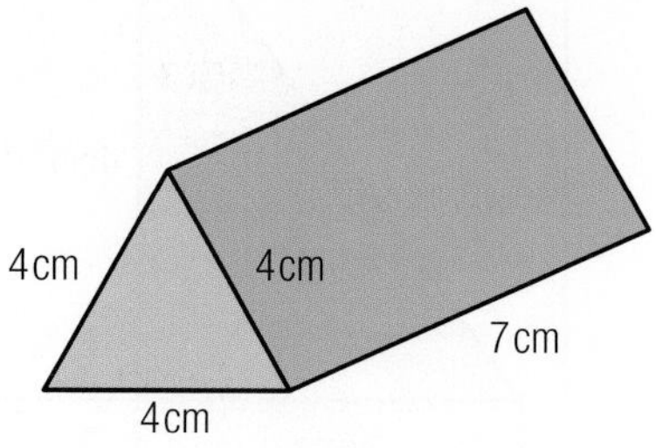

4cm 4cm

7cm

4cm

a triangular prism

3

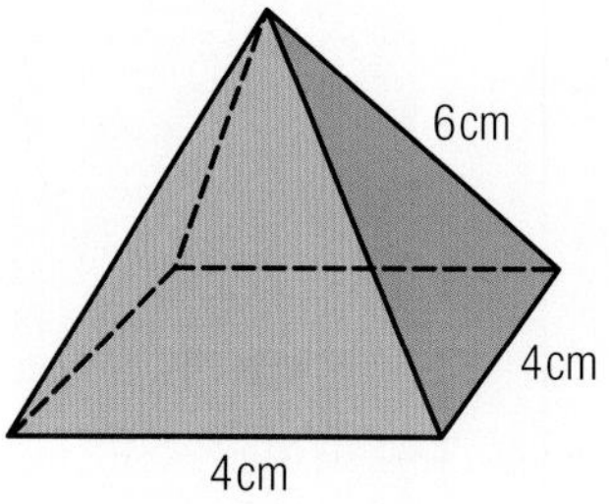

6cm

4cm

4cm

a square-based pyramid

4

All the faces are equilateral triangles.

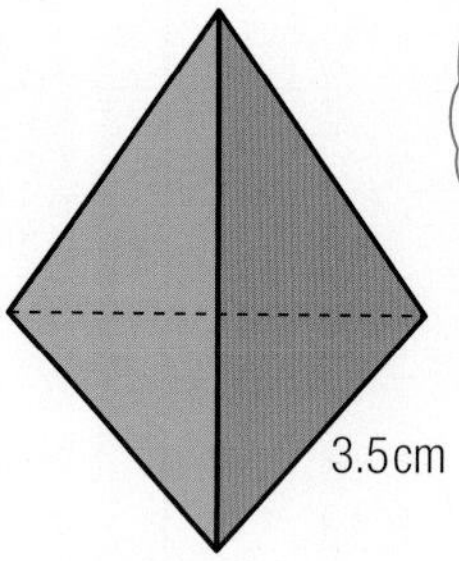

3.5cm

a regular tetrahedron

5 ★

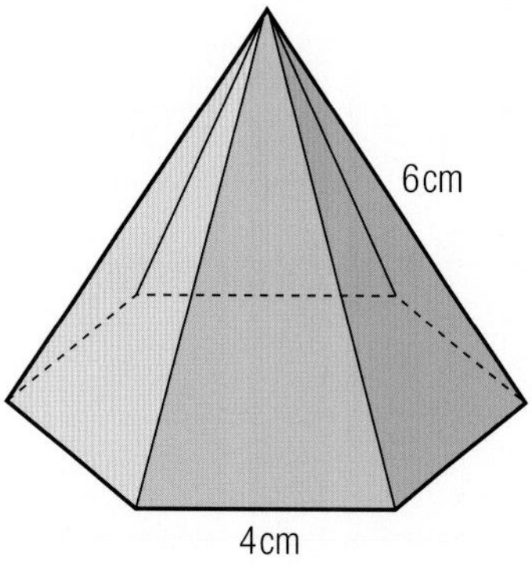

6cm

4cm

a hexagonal-based pyramid

6

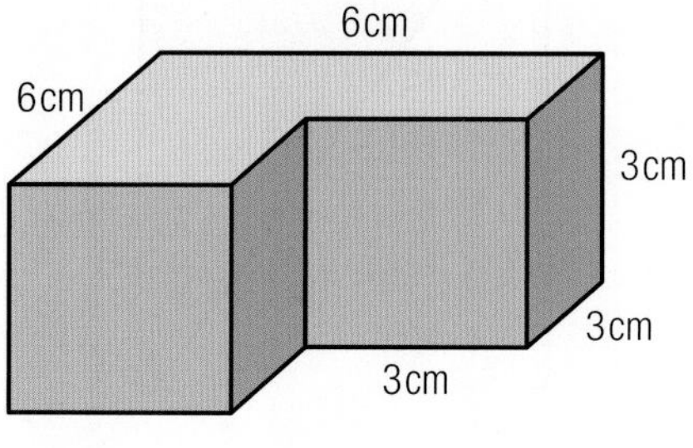

6cm

6cm

3cm

3cm

3cm

a prism

Surface area of three-dimensional shapes

You already know that the **surface area** of a three-dimensional shape is the total area of all of its faces. This is easily calculated if a net of the shape is drawn.

Worked example

Here is a net of a triangular prism. Calculate the surface area of the prism.

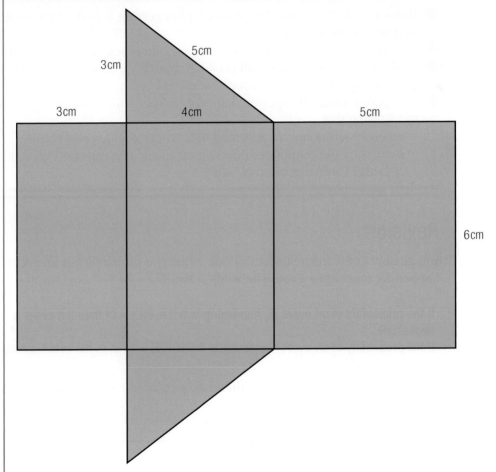

Area of each triangular face = $\frac{1}{2} \times 4 \times 3 = 6\,\text{cm}^2$
Area of rectangular faces = $6 \times (3 + 4 + 5) = 6 \times 12 = 72\,\text{cm}^2$
Total area = surface area of prism = $6 + 6 + 72 = 84\,\text{cm}^2$

EXERCISE 25.2

Calculate the surface area of each of the three-dimensional objects in Exercise 25.1.

Measure the heights of any triangular faces accurately, using a ruler.

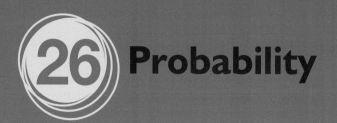

Probability

Know that if the probability of an event occurring is p, then the probability of it not occurring is $1 - p$.

Find probabilities based on equally likely outcomes in practical contexts.

Find and list systematically all possible mutually exclusive outcomes for single events and for two successive events.

Compare estimated experimental probabilities with theoretical probabilities, recognising that:

- when experiments are repeated different outcomes may result
- increasing the number of times an experiment is repeated generally leads to better estimates of probability.

Revision

You already know from Student's Book 1 that the probability of an event happening must have a value between 0 and 1.

> If the probability of an event (E) happening is 0 (i.e. P(E) = 0) then the event is impossible.
> If the probability of an event happening is 1 (i.e. P(E) = 1) then the event is certain.

The probability of any event can therefore be placed somewhere on a probability scale like this.

$$0 \qquad \tfrac{1}{2} \qquad 1$$

EXERCISE 26.1

1 **a)** An ordinary six-sided dice is rolled. Calculate the probability:
   (i) of getting a 3
   (ii) of not getting a 3.
   b) What do you notice about the sum of your answers in part **a)**?

2 A weighted six-sided dice is rolled. If $P(6) = \frac{1}{3}$, calculate the probability:
   a) of not getting a 6
   b) of either getting a 6 or not getting a 6.

3 **a)** A coloured spinner is spun. It has three colours: red, blue and yellow.
   If P(red) = $\frac{1}{8}$ and P(blue) = $\frac{3}{8}$, calculate:
   (i)   P(yellow)
   (ii) P(not red)
   (iii) P(not blue).
   b) What is the sum of P(blue) and P(not blue)?

You will have noticed in Exercise 26.1 that the probability of an event happening and the probability of the event not happening are related.

> **If the probability of an event happening is _p_, then the probability of the event not happening is 1 − _p_.**

Combined events

Combined events are about probability involving two or more events.

Worked example

Two coins are tossed.
a)   Show all the possible outcomes in a two-way table.

b)   Calculate the probability:
   (i) of getting two heads
   (ii) of getting a head and a tail in any order.

a)

		Coin 1	
		Head	Tail
Coin 2	Head	head, head	tail, head
	Tail	head, tail	tail, tail

b) **(i)**   All four outcomes are equally likely, therefore the probability of getting
        head, head is $\frac{1}{4}$.

   (ii) The probability of getting a head and a tail in any order, i.e. head, tail or
        tail, head is $\frac{2}{4} = \frac{1}{2}$.

EXERCISE 26.2

1 **a)** Two tetrahedral dice are rolled. If each is numbered 1–4, draw a two-way table to show all the possible outcomes.
   b) What is the probability that both dice show even numbers?
   c) What is the probability that the number on one dice is 1 less than the number on the other?
   d) What is the probability that the sum of both numbers is odd?

2 **a)** A four-sided and a six-sided dice are rolled. Copy and complete the two-way table to show all the possible combinations.

		Dice 1			
		1	2	3	4
Dice 2	1	1, 1			
	2				
	3				
	4				
	5		2, 5		
	6				

What is the probability:
b) of getting a double 3
c) of not getting a double 3
d) of getting any double
e) of getting a total score of 6
f) of not getting a total score of 6
g) of getting a total score of 11
h) of getting an even number on both dice
i) of getting an even number on at least one dice
j) of getting scores which differ by 2
k) of getting a result in which the score on dice 1 is greater than that on dice 2?

3 The two-way table below shows the age and gender of people on a bus.

		Age			
		Under 10	10–20	21–50	Over 50
Gender	Female	2	8	12	6
	Male	4	5	18	5

a) How many people were on the bus?
   One of these people is picked at random.
b) What is the probability that the person is female?
c) What is the probability that the person is aged 21–50?
d) What is the probability that the person is a male aged under 10?

4 The weather on each of the days in January, February and March of a
particular year was recorded. Each day's weather was recorded as either
rainy, cloudy or sunny. The results are shown in this two-way table.

		Weather		
		Rainy	Cloudy	Sunny
Month	January	8	18	5
	February	14	12	2
	March	6	8	17

a) How many days were sunny?
b) How many days were rainy?

If one of these days is picked at random, what is the probability that:
c) it was a sunny day
d) it was a day in February
e) it was a rainy day in January?

Experimental and theoretical probabilities

You already know that when an ordinary six-sided dice is rolled, the probability
of getting a 4 is $\frac{1}{6}$. This is called the **theoretical probability**. In theory, there is a
1 in 6 chance of getting a score of 4.

If the dice is then rolled ten times and the number 4 occurs three times, the
probability of getting a 4 is $\frac{3}{10}$. This is called the **experimental probability**. The
experimental probability is calculated from the results of the experiment. If the
dice was rolled 100 times and the number 4 occurred 20 times, the experimental
probability of getting a 4 would then be $\frac{20}{100}$ or $\frac{1}{5}$.

*Notice that the theoretical
probability and the experimental
probability need not be the same.*

EXERCISE 26.3

1 Choose a fair coin.
   a) What is the theoretical probability of getting a head?
   b) Flip the coin five times and record the results. What is the experimental probability of getting a head?
   c) Flip the coin another five times and record the results. Using all ten results, what is the experimental probability of getting a head?
   d) Flip the coin another ten times and record the results. Using all 20 results, what is the experimental probability of getting a head?
   e) Combine your results with those of four friends. Using all 100 results, what is the experimental probability of getting a head?

2 **a)** Repeat all of question 1, using the same coins.
   b) Did you get the same answers as before?

3 Choose a fair six-sided dice.
   a) What is the theoretical probability of getting a 1?
   b) Roll the dice five times and record the results. What is the experimental probability of getting a 1?
   c) Roll the dice another five times and record the results. Using all ten results, what is the experimental probability of getting a 1?
   d) Roll the dice another ten times and record the results. Using all 20 results, what is the experimental probability of getting a 1?
   e) Combine your results with those of nine friends. Using all 200 results, what is the experimental probability of getting a 1?
   f) How did your experimental probabilities compare with the theoretical probability?
   g) Did the experimental probabilities change as the number of rolls increased?

4 **a)** Repeat all of question 3, using the same dice.
   b) Did you get the same answers as before?

From your experiments in Exercise 26.3 you may have noticed that:

- Experimental probabilities may be different from the theoretical probability.
- The same experiment may produce different results when it is repeated.
- Generally, the more times an experiment is carried out, the closer the experimental probability gets to the theoretical probability.

Compare your results with these points. Is this what your results showed?

27 Calculations and mental strategies 4

◆ Use known facts and place value to multiply and divide simple fractions.
◆ Use known facts and place value to multiply and divide simple decimals,
   e.g. 0.07×9, $2.4 \div 3$.
◆ Solve simple word problems including direct proportion problems.
◆ Multiply and divide integers and decimals by decimals such as 0.6 or 0.06,
   understanding where to place the decimal point by considering equivalent
   calculations, e.g. $4.37 \times 0.3 = (4.37 \times 3) \div 10$, $92.4 \div 0.06 = (92.4 \times 100) \div 6$.

Mental strategies

You already know from Chapter 13 that you can use basic multiplication facts to
work out more complicated multiplications in your head.

EXERCISE 27.1A

Multiply the following pairs of numbers in your head, without looking at a
multiplication grid or using a calculator. Write down your answers.

1	**a)** 6×9	**b)** 10×9	**c)** 16×9
2	**a)** 5×7	**b)** 10×7	**c)** 15×7
3	**a)** 8×3	**b)** 40×3	**c)** 48×3
4	**a)** 9×2	**b)** 80×2	**c)** 89×2
5	**a)** 8×7	**b)** 30×7	**c)** 38×7
6	**a)** 5×9	**b)** 30×9	**c)** 35×9
7	**a)** 23×4	**b)** 41×5	**c)** 67×7
8	**a)** 42×4	**b)** 51×7	**c)** 83×9

EXERCISE 27.1B

Work with a partner and ask each other the following questions. Do them in your head.

One of you asks part **a)**, the other asks part **b)**.

1	**a)** $56 \div 8$	**b)** $45 \div 9$
2	**a)** $72 \div 9$	**b)** $72 \div 8$
3	**a)** $24 \div 3$	**b)** $84 \div 7$
4	**a)** $81 \div 9$	**b)** $78 \div 2$
5	**a)** $72 \div 4$	**b)** $55 \div 5$
6	**a)** $60 \div 5$	**b)** $96 \div 3$
7	**a)** $93 \div 3$	**b)** $90 \div 6$
8	**a)** $96 \div 6$	**b)** $147 \div 7$
9	**a)** $75 \div 5$	**b)** $279 \div 9$
10	**a)** $81 \div 3$	**b)** $132 \div 3$
11	**a)** $154 \div 7$	**b)** $168 \div 6$
12	**a)** $729 \div 9$	**b)** $424 \div 8$

EXERCISE 27.1C

Without doing any division, state whether each of the following numbers is divisible:

a) by 5   **b)** by 6   **c)** by 9.

1	308	**2**	342
3	240	**4**	445
5	167	**6**	3085
7	2772	**8**	3963
9	3969	**10**	4410

You can use basic multiplication facts to work out calculations involving fractions mentally.

Worked examples

a) Work out $\frac{4}{5} \times 10$.

This is equivalent to $\frac{4}{5} \times \frac{10}{1}$.

$\frac{4}{5} \times \frac{10}{1} = \frac{40}{5} = 8$

b) Calculate $\frac{3}{4} \div \frac{1}{4}$.

This is equivalent to $\frac{3}{4} \times \frac{4}{1}$.

$\frac{3}{4} \times \frac{4}{1} = \frac{12}{4} = 3$

EXERCISE 27.1D

1 Work out these multiplications in your head.

   a) $\frac{3}{2} \times 2$ **b)** $\frac{3}{2} \times 4$ **c)** $\frac{4}{5} \times 5$ **d)** $\frac{4}{5} \times 15$ **e)** $\frac{7}{8} \times 8$

   f) $\frac{7}{8} \times 4$ **g)** $\frac{3}{4} \times 12$ **h)** $\frac{4}{7} \times 14$ **i)** $\frac{5}{8} \times \frac{4}{5}$ **j)** $\frac{3}{4} \times \frac{8}{9}$

2 Work out these divisions in your head.

   a) $\frac{2}{3} \div 2$ **b)** $\frac{4}{5} \div 4$ **c)** $\frac{4}{5} \div 8$ **d)** $\frac{7}{8} \div 7$ **e)** $\frac{8}{9} \div 4$

   f) $\frac{3}{4} \div \frac{1}{2}$ **g)** $\frac{3}{5} \div \frac{3}{5}$ **h)** $\frac{4}{7} \div \frac{2}{7}$ **i)** $\frac{3}{8} \div \frac{3}{4}$ **j)** $\frac{1}{2} \div \frac{1}{3}$

You can use basic multiplication facts to work out calculations involving decimals mentally. Think carefully about place value and where to place the decimal point.

EXERCISE 27.1E

1 Work out these multiplications in your head.

   a) 7×9 **b)** 7×0.9 **c)** 0.7×9 **d)** 7×0.09

   e) 7×0.9 **f)** 6×8 **g)** 0.6×8 **h)** 0.6×0.8

   i) 5×7 **j)** 0.5×7

2 Work out these divisions in your head.

   a) $24 \div 3$ **b)** $2.4 \div 3$ **c)** $24 \div 0.3$ **d)** $2.4 \div 0.3$

   e) $5.2 \div 4$ **f)** $5.2 \div 0.4$ **g)** $6.3 \div 9$ **h)** $6.3 \div 0.9$

   i) $8.4 \div 7$ **j)** $8.4 \div 0.7$

You can use basic multiplication facts in problems involving ratios and proportion.

✪ Worked example

The ratios 5 to 8 and 15 to _____ are equivalent (in proportion).
What is the missing number?
15 = 3 × 5, so the missing number is 3 × 8 = 24.

EXERCISE 27.1F

Find the missing numbers so that the ratios in each pair are equivalent (in proportion).

1 2 to 3 and 4 to _____

2 5 to 9 and _____ to 27

3 6 to _____ and 3 to 10

4 8 to 7 and _____ to 21

5 1 to 5 and 5 to _____

6 6 to 7 and _____ to 77

7 4 to 1 and 12 to _____

8 6 to 5 and _____ to 30

9 1 to 10 and 5 to _____

10 4 to 3 and _____ to 39

EXERCISE 27.1G

Solve these problems in your head.

1 Two apples cost 60 cents. How much do five cost?

2 Three stamps cost $1.20. How much do four cost?

3 Six eggs cost $0.60. How much do 18 cost?

4 Two cinema tickets cost $7. How much do three cost?

5 Three bricks are 20 cm tall. How tall are 12 bricks?

6 Five rods are 1 m long altogether. How long are eight rods?

7 A line of three identical cars parked end to end is 15 m long. How long is a line of five of these cars?

8 Two oil tanks hold 1500 litres. How much do five tanks hold?

9 Two eggs take 4 minutes to boil. How long will five eggs take to boil in the same pan?

10 Three men get wet in rain in 5 minutes. How long will it take 10 men to get wet in the same storm?

Written methods

You already know how to multiply a number by a decimal. You can use place value to help you multiply a decimal by a decimal.

Worked examples

a) Multiply 4.37×3.

$$
\begin{array}{r}
4.3\ 7 \\
\times \qquad 3 \\
\hline
1\ 3.1\ 1
\end{array}
$$

Therefore $4.37 \times 3 = 13.11$.

b) Multiply 4.37×0.3.

This is equivalent to $4.37 \times \frac{3}{10}$.

$$4.37 \times \frac{3}{10} = (4.37 \times 3) \div 10$$
$$= 13.11 \div 10$$
$$= 1.311$$

Therefore $4.37 \times 0.3 = 1.311$.

EXERCISE 27.2A

Without using a calculator, work out these multiplications.

1	**a)** 6.51×5	**b)** 6.51×0.5	**c)** 6.51×0.05
2	**a)** 3.84×6	**b)** 3.84×0.6	**c)** 3.84×0.06
3	**a)** 5.41×3	**b)** 5.41×0.3	**c)** 5.41×0.03
4	**a)** 7.93×4	**b)** 7.93×0.4	**c)** 7.93×0.04
5	**a)** 8.47×5	**b)** 8.47×0.5	**c)** 8.47×0.05
6	**a)** 5.39×6	**b)** 5.35×0.6	**c)** 5.39×0.06
7	**a)** 7.44×7	**b)** 7.44×0.7	**c)** 7.44×0.07
8	**a)** 2.12×8	**b)** 2.12×0.8	**c)** 2.12×0.08
9	**a)** 1.03×9	**b)** 1.03×0.9	**c)** 1.03×0.09
10	**a)** 2.73×2	**b)** 2.73×0.2	**c)** 2.73×0.02

You can divide a decimal by a whole number either mentally or by short division. You can use place value to help you divide a decimal by a decimal.

Worked examples

a) Calculate $8.73 \div 3$.

$$
\begin{array}{r}
2.\ 9\ 1 \\
3\overline{)\ 8.^2 7\ 3}
\end{array}
$$

Therefore $8.73 \div 3 = 2.91$.

Similarly,
$8.73 \div 0.03 = 2.91 \times 100 = 291.$

b) Calculate $8.73 \div 0.3$.

This is equivalent to $8.73 \div \frac{3}{10}$.

$$8.73 \div \frac{3}{10} = 8.73 \times \frac{10}{3}$$
$$= (8.73 \div 3) \times 10$$
$$= 2.91 \times 10$$
$$= 29.1$$

Therefore $8.73 \div 0.3 = 29.1$.

EXERCISE 27.2B

Without using a calculator work out these divisions.

	a)	b)	c)
1	5.31 ÷ 3	5.31 ÷ 0.3	5.31 ÷ 0.03
2	6.74 ÷ 2	6.74 ÷ 0.2	6.74 ÷ 0.02
3	9.66 ÷ 3	9.66 ÷ 0.3	9.66 ÷ 0.03
4	8.48 ÷ 4	8.48 ÷ 0.4	8.48 ÷ 0.04
5	7.65 ÷ 5	7.65 ÷ 0.5	7.65 ÷ 0.05
6	12.72 ÷ 6	12.72 ÷ 0.6	12.72 ÷ 0.06
7	22.19 ÷ 7	22.19 ÷ 0.7	22.19 ÷ 0.07
8	44.56 ÷ 8	44.56 ÷ 0.8	44.56 ÷ 0.08
9	36.36 ÷ 9	36.36 ÷ 0.9	36.36 ÷ 0.09
10	0.06 ÷ 3	0.06 ÷ 0.3	0.06 ÷ 0.03

EXERCISE 27.2C

Work out these calculations. Think carefully where to place the decimal point.

	a)	b)
1	6.24 × 3	6.24 × 0.03
2	6.24 ÷ 3	6.24 ÷ 0.03
3	5.9 × 5	5.9 × 0.05
4	5.9 ÷ 5	5.9 ÷ 0.05
5	8.33 × 7	8.33 × 0.07
6	8.33 ÷ 7	8.33 ÷ 0.07
7	4 ÷ 8	4 ÷ 0.08
8	4 × 8	4 × 0.008
9	6 × 7	6 × 0.07
10	3 ÷ 2	3 ÷ 0.02

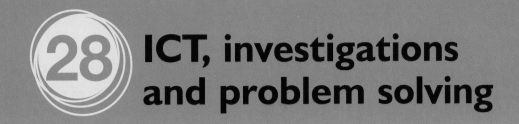

28 ICT, investigations and problem solving

1 Nets of a cube

In Chapter 25 you saw these three nets of a cube.

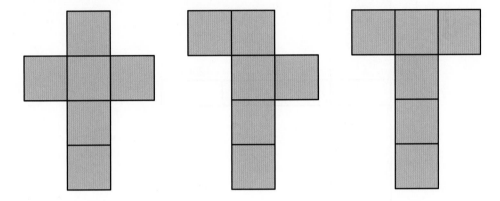

a) Copy the nets above, cut them out and see that each one folds to make a cube.

b) If you rotate a net or turn it over it is still the same net. There are 11 *different* nets of a cube (not counting nets made by rotating or turning the paper over). As a pair or in a group, see how many you can draw.

c) A net of a cube can have four or three or two squares in a row. Why is it not possible for a net of a cube to have five squares in a row?

d) Choose a different solid shape. How many different nets can you draw for it?

2 Packaging

Cereal packet designers need to make sure that the amount of card used to make the packet is kept to a minimum in order to keep costs down.

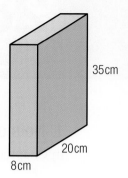

A cereal packet manufacturer needs to design a net for a cereal packet of these dimensions.

One of the packet designers produced this net:

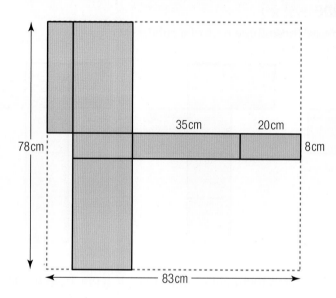

However, this is not a very efficient net because, although it folds to make the packet, it needs to be cut from a rectangular piece of card with dimensions 78 cm × 83 cm. This means that this net needs to be cut from a rectangular piece of card of area 6474 cm².

a) Your challenge is to produce a number of different nets which:

- fold to produce the packet
- are cut from smaller rectangular pieces of card than in the example above.

Use your drawings for the net of a cube from investigation 1.

b) What is the smallest rectangular piece of card possible, on which a net of the cereal packet can be drawn?

3 Experimental probability of heads

In this activity you will use a spreadsheet to analyse what happens to the results of an experiment, as you repeat it more and more times.

a) Set up a spreadsheet with the headings shown in the example.

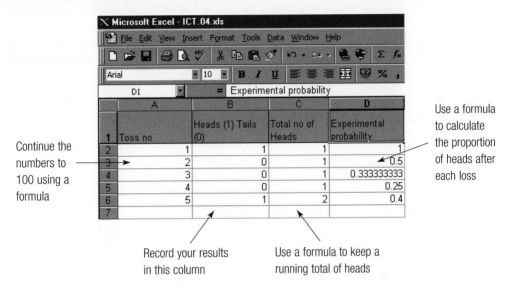

Continue the numbers to 100 using a formula

Use a formula to calculate the proportion of heads after each loss

Record your results in this column

Use a formula to keep a running total of heads

b) Toss a coin 100 times. Each time record the result in your spreadsheet. Use a 1 for a head and a 0 for a tail.

c) Enter formulae in your spreadsheet to calculate the total number of heads and the experimental probability of heads.

d) Plot a line graph to show how the experimental probability of heads changes as the number of tosses increases.

e) Explain what your graph shows.

⭐ **f)** Do a similar experiment to see if, when dropped, a drawing pin falls 'pin up' more times than it falls 'pin down'.

Review 4A

1   A man is paid $60.80 for an 8-hour working day. How much will he be paid for a 42-hour week?

2   An alloy is made of nickel and tungsten in the ratio $3:5$. How much nickel is there in 2.4 kg of this alloy?

3   The formulae for converting between Celsius and Fahrenheit are:
$$F = \tfrac{9}{5}C + 32 \quad \text{and} \quad C = \tfrac{5}{9}(F - 32)$$

   a) Convert 105 °C to degrees Fahrenheit.
   b) Convert 113 °F to degrees Celsius.

4   A formula for calculating displacement (distance from a given point) is:
$$s = ut + \tfrac{1}{2}at^2$$

   a) Calculate s when $u = 4$, $t = 5$ and $a = 6$.
   b) Calculate a when $s = 50$, $u = 2$ and $t = 6$.

5   **a)** Draw this triangle on a coordinate grid, with its vertices at the points given.
   b) Enlarge the triangle by a scale factor of 2 with $A = (-3, 2)$ as the centre of enlargement.

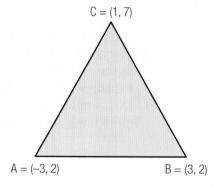

6   Draw a possible net of this square-based pyramid. Use a pair of compasses where appropriate.

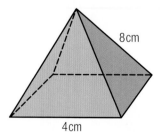

7 A box contains six triangular tokens and four circular tokens. They are numbered as shown.

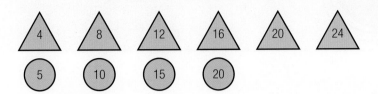

One token is picked out of the box at random. Calculate the probability that:
a) it is circular
b) the number is a multiple of 3
c) the number is prime.

8 Work out the following. Think carefully where to place the decimal point.
a) (i) 8.21×3 **(ii)** 16.42×0.03
b) (i) $11.37 \div 3$ **(ii)** $22.74 \div 0.03$
c) (i) 2.9×5 **(ii)** 5.8×0.05
d) (i) $7.55 \div 5$ **(ii)** $22.65 \div 0.05$

1 Seven pens cost $0.42.
   a) What will 5000 pens cost?
   b) There is a special offer. If you buy 5000 pens there is a 75% discount. What will 5000 pens cost with the special offer?

2 The sizes of the angles of a triangle are in the ratio $5:6:7$. What size is each angle?

3 Copy and complete these so that the ratios in each pair are equivalent (in proportion).
   a) 2 to 7 and 14 to _____   **b)** 5 to 3 and _____ to 27
   c) 6 to _____ and 18 to 51

4 In each part, the values of three of v, u, a and t are given.
   Use the formula $v = u + at$ to form an equation and find the missing value.
   a) $v = 44$, $a = 4$ and $t = 6$ **b)** $v = 150$, $t = 5$ and $u = 20$

5 A formula for calculating displacement (distance from a point) is
$$s = ut + \tfrac{1}{2} at^2$$

   a) Calculate s when $u = 5$, $t = 7$ and $a = 4$.
   b) Calculate u when $s = 120$, $a = 2$ and $t = 4$.

6 **a)** Make a scale drawing of this diagram, using a scale of 1 cm = 10 km.
   b) Measure the lengths AB and BC in centimetres.
   c) What are the actual lengths of AB and BC in kilometres?
   d) Measure the size of the angle x.

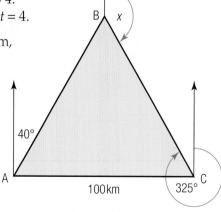

7 Sketch a possible net of the cuboid below. Mark all the dimensions clearly.

8 A bag contains five white balls, eight green balls and 12 blue balls.
   A ball is picked at random.
   Calculate the probability that it is:
   a) white   **b)** not white
   c) blue   **d)** white or blue.

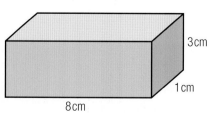

Index